# EXPLORE LONDON

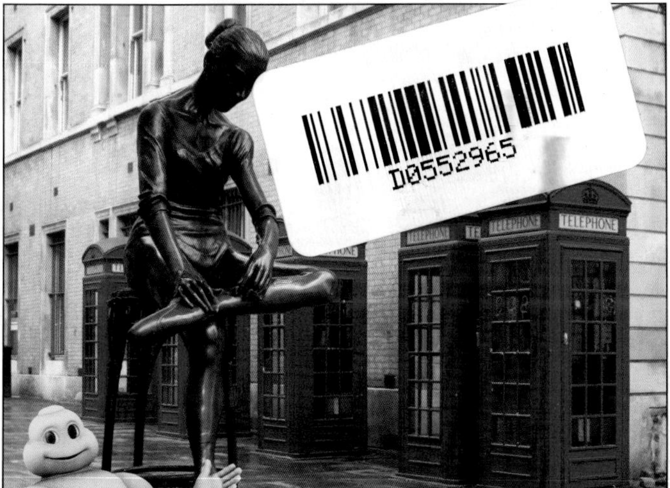

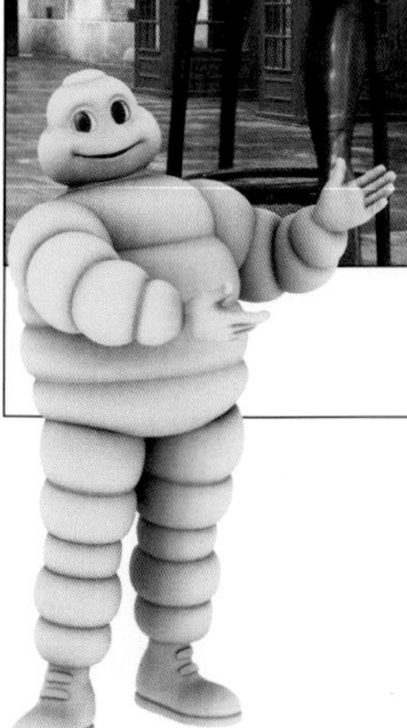

This I-SPY book belongs to:____________________

# Central London

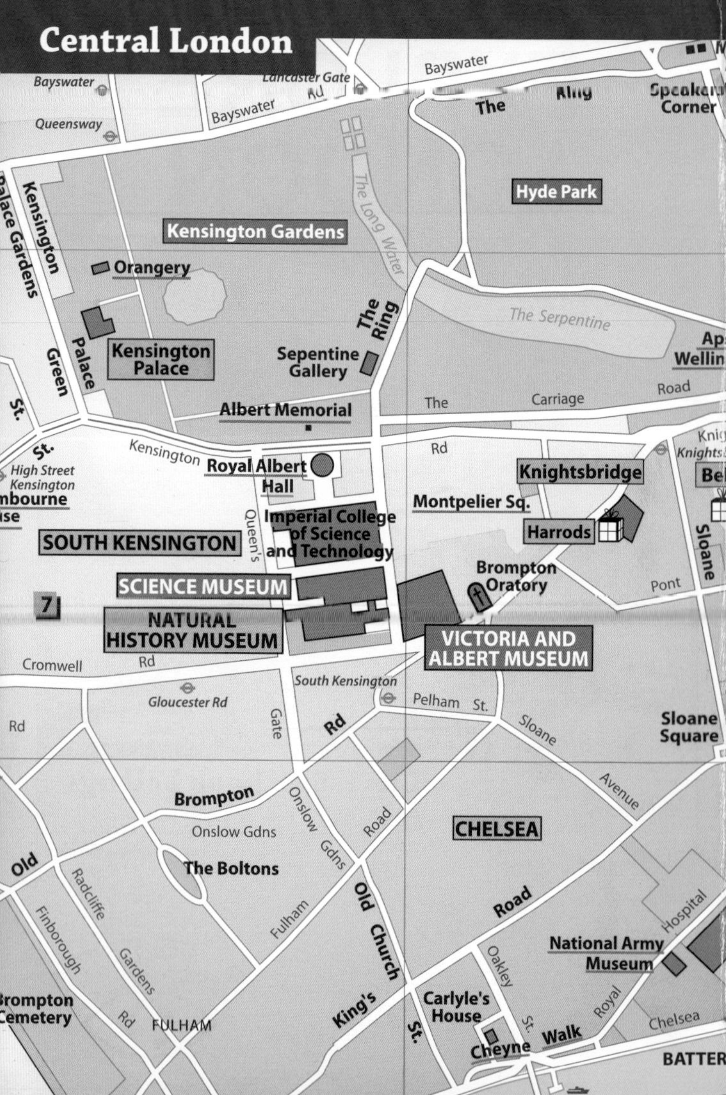

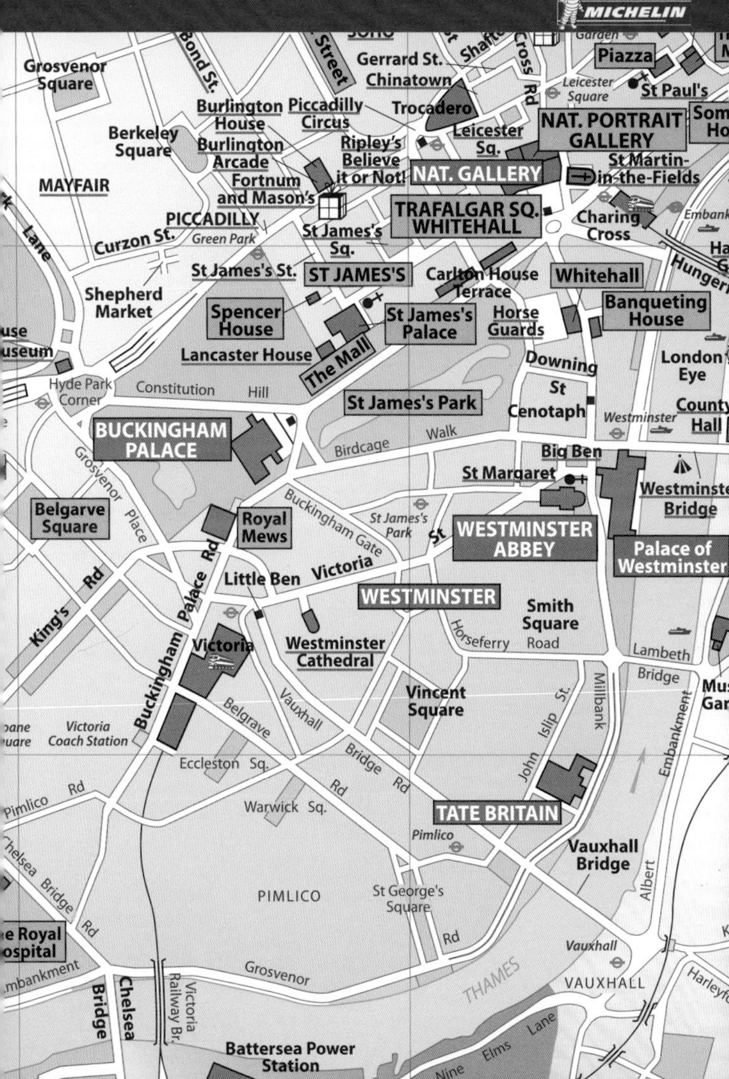
Grosvenor Square
Bond St.
Street
Gerrard St.
Chinatown
Cross Rd
Leicester Square
Piazza
St Paul's
Burlington House
Piccadilly Circus
Trocadero
Berkeley Square
Burlington Arcade
Ripley's Believe it or Not!
Leicester Sq.
NAT. PORTRAIT GALLERY
MAYFAIR
Fortnum and Mason's
NAT. GALLERY
St Martin-in-the-Fields
PICCADILLY
Curzon St.
Green Park
St James's Sq.
TRAFALGAR SQ. WHITEHALL
Charing Cross
Lane
Shepherd Market
St James's St.
ST JAMES'S
Carlton House Terrace
Whitehall
Spencer House
St James's Palace
Horse Guards
Banqueting House
Lancaster House
The Mall
Downing
London Eye
Hyde Park Corner
Constitution Hill
St James's Park
St
Cenotaph
County Hall
Westminster
BUCKINGHAM PALACE
Birdcage Walk
Big Ben
Grosvenor Place
St Margaret
Westminster Bridge
Belgarve Square
Royal Mews
Buckingham Gate
St James's Park
WESTMINSTER ABBEY
Palace of Westminster
King's Rd
Palace Rd
Little Ben
Victoria St
WESTMINSTER
Smith Square
Buckingham
Victoria
Westminster Cathedral
Horseferry Road
Lambeth Bridge
Millbank
Vincent Square
Belgrave
Vauxhall
Islip St.
Victoria Coach Station
Embankment
Eccleston Sq.
Bridge Rd
John
Pimlico Rd
Rd
Warwick Sq.
TATE BRITAIN
Pimlico
Vauxhall Bridge
Chelsea Bridge
Albert
PIMLICO
St George's Square
Rd
Vauxhall
Grosvenor
THAMES
VAUXHALL
Embankment
Bridge
Chelsea
Victoria Railway Br.
Lane
Elms
Nine
Battersea Power Station

# Central London

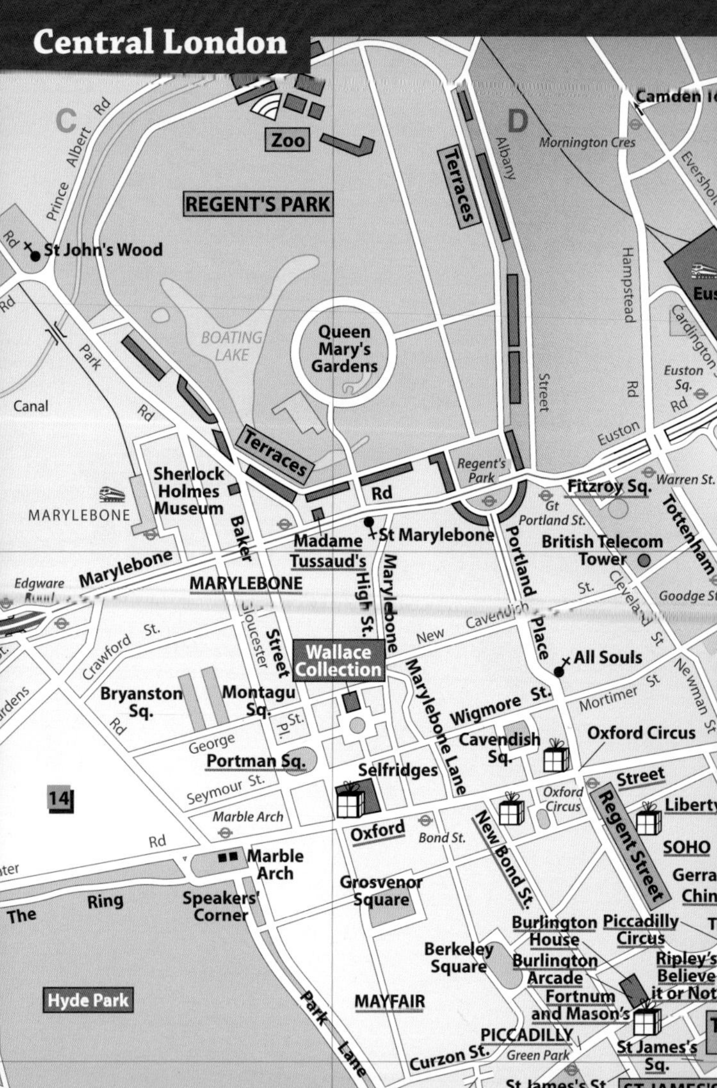

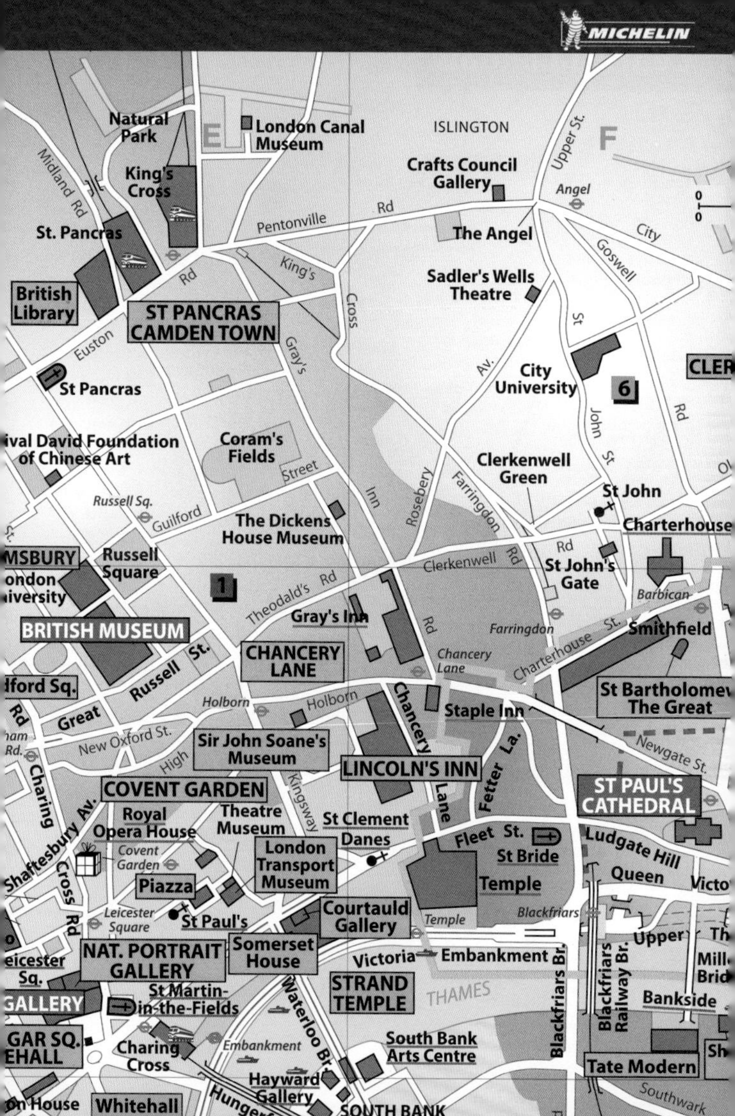

Natural Park
London Canal Museum
ISLINGTON
E
F
King's Cross
Crafts Council Gallery
Upper St.
Angel
Midland Rd
St. Pancras
Pentonville
Rd
The Angel
City
Goswell
King's
Rd
Sadler's Wells Theatre
British Library
ST PANCRAS CAMDEN TOWN
Cross
St
Euston
Gray's
CLER
St Pancras
City University
Av.
6
John
Rd
ival David Foundation of Chinese Art
Coram's Fields
Street
Clerkenwell Green
St
Russell Sq.
Guilford
Inn
Rosebery
Farringdon
St John
The Dickens House Museum
Charterhouse
MSBURY
Russell Square
Clerkenwell
Rd
Rd
ondon iversity
1
St John's Gate
Theobald's Rd
Barbican
BRITISH MUSEUM
Gray's Inn
Rd
Farringdon
St.
Smithfield
St.
CHANCERY LANE
Chancery Lane
Charterhouse
Russell
dford Sq.
Holborn
Holborn
Staple Inn
St Bartholomew The Great
Rd
Great
Chancery
Fetter La.
New Oxford St.
Newgate St.
Sir John Soane's Museum
High
LINCOLN'S INN
Charing
Kingsway
COVENT GARDEN
ST PAUL'S CATHEDRAL
Av.
Royal Opera House
Theatre Museum
St Clement Danes
Lane
Fleet St.
Shaftesbury
London Transport Museum
Ludgate Hill
Covent Garden
St Bride
Queen
Victo
Cross
Piazza
Temple
Leicester Square
St Paul's
Courtauld Gallery
Temple
Blackfriars
Rd
Upper
Th
NAT. PORTRAIT GALLERY
Somerset House
Victoria
Embankment
Br.
Mill Brid
eicester Sq.
STRAND TEMPLE
THAMES
Blackfriars
Blackfriars Railway Br.
Bankside
GALLERY
St Martin-in-the-Fields
Waterloo Br.
GAR SQ. EHALL
Charing Cross
Embankment
South Bank Arts Centre
Tate Modern
Hayward Gallery
Southwark
on House
Whitehall
Hungerf
SOUTH BANK

# Central London

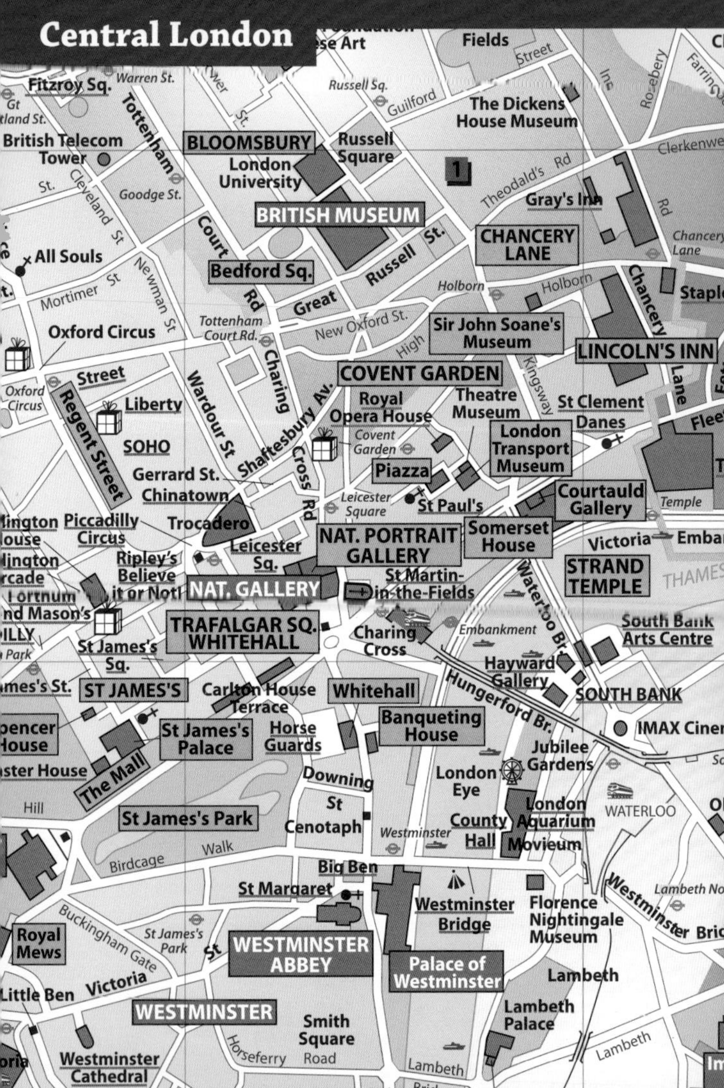

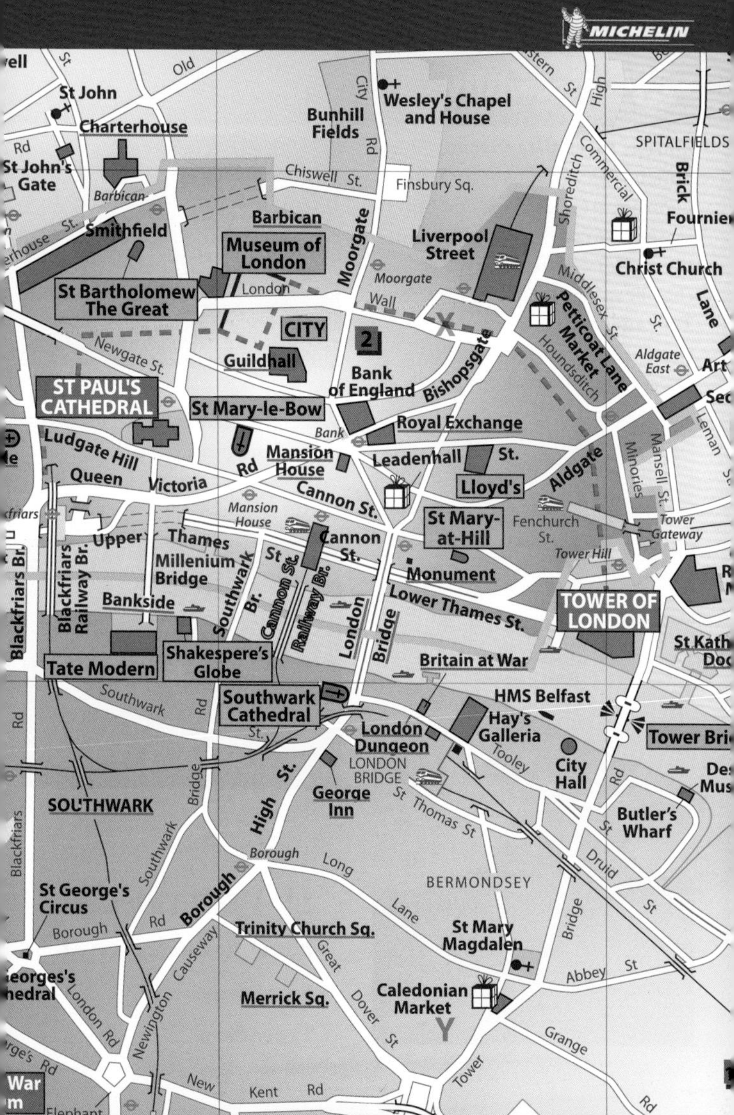
MICHELIN
St John
Charterhouse
St John's Gate
Barbican
Smithfield
St Bartholomew The Great
Museum of London
Barbican
Bunhill Fields
Wesley's Chapel and House
Chiswell St.
Finsbury Sq.
Moorgate
Liverpool Street
SPITALFIELDS
Christ Church
Petticoat Lane Market
CITY
Guildhall
Bank of England
Bishopsgate
ST PAUL'S CATHEDRAL
St Mary-le-Bow
Royal Exchange
Ludgate Hill
Mansion House
Leadenhall St.
Lloyd's
Aldgate
Cannon St.
St Mary-at-Hill
Fenchurch St.
Tower Hill
Tower Gateway
Millenium Bridge
Monument
Lower Thames St.
TOWER OF LONDON
Bankside
Tate Modern
Shakespere's Globe
Britain at War
Southwark Cathedral
HMS Belfast
Hay's Galleria
London Dungeon
LONDON BRIDGE
City Hall
Tower Bri
George Inn
Butler's Wharf
SOUTHWARK
BERMONDSEY
St George's Circus
Trinity Church Sq.
St Mary Magdalen
Merrick Sq.
Caledonian Market
Elephant

# I-SPY Piccadilly

Start at **Piccadilly Circus**, famous the world over for its neon advertising signs and the statue of **Eros** dedicated to the Earl of Shaftesbury for his charity work. Behind you is the **Trocadero**, a haven of sound, computer games and special effects covering seven storeys.

*Piccadilly Circus*

*Eros Statue*

Walk up Piccadilly which takes its name from piccadill, a shirt collar fashionable in the seventeenth century.

*Trocadero*

## I-SPY Tick List:

- **Piccadilly Circus** 
- **Eros Statue**
- **Trocadero**

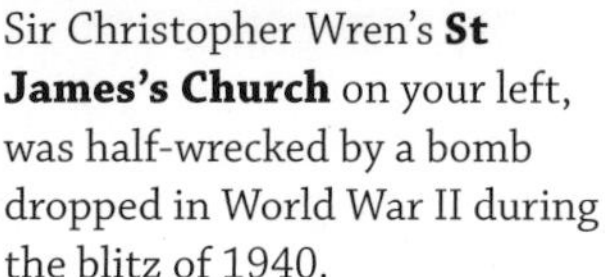

*Fortnum and Mason*

*Royal Academy of Arts*

*Burlington Arcade*

Sir Christopher Wren's **St James's Church** on your left, was half-wrecked by a bomb dropped in World War II during the blitz of 1940.

Further on is **Fortnum and Mason's** famous provisions and general store founded in 1707. Every hour, figures of the founders emerge from the Fortnum and Mason Clock to see how trade is doing. Almost opposite is The **Royal Academy of Arts** in Burlington House and next to that **Burlington Arcade** with its exclusive shops patrolled by former 10th Hussars dressed as **Regency beadles**.

## I-SPY Tick List:

- **St James's Church** ○
- **Fortnum and Mason** ○
- **Royal Academy of Arts** ○
- **Burlington Arcade** ○
- **Regency Beadles** ○

#  Buckingham Palace

Ritz Hotel

Green Park

The famous **Ritz Hotel**, built in 1906 is one of London's earliest steel-frame buildings. Next you will come to **Green Park**. Walk down through the park, as King Charles II was fond of doing. Soon you will see the **Victoria Memorial** in front of Her Majesty the Queen's London residence, **Buckingham Palace**.

 I-SPY Tick List:

- **Ritz Hotel** ○
- **Green Park** ○
- **Victoria Memorial** ○
- **Buckingham Palace** ○

Buckingham Palace and Victoria Memorial

# Buckingham Palace

*Gold Stage Coach*

The Royal Art Collection can be seen in the **Queen's Gallery** and horse drawn carriages and motorcars in the **Royal Mews**. The magnificent **State Rooms** are open to the public in summer.

*Queen's Gallery*

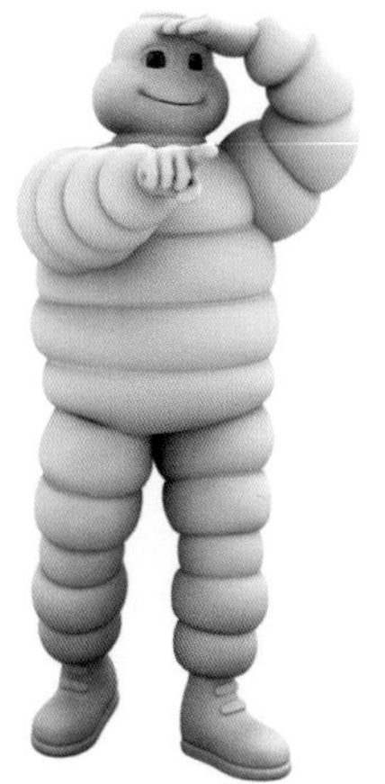

## I-SPY Tick List:

- **Queen's Gallery** ○
- **Royal Mews** ○
- **State Rooms** ○

# I-SPY The Mall

Walk up **The Mall**, with its distinctive red tarmac, leaving Buckingham Palace behind you. On the right is **St James's Park**; on the left **Clarence House** and **St James's Palace**.

*The Mall*

*St James's Palace*

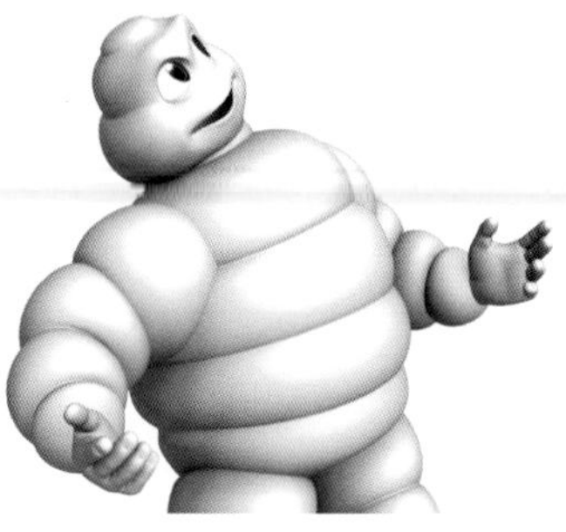

I-SPY Tick List:

- **The Mall** ○
- **St James's Park** ○
- **Clarence House** ○
- **St James's Palace** ○

*Queen Mother Statue*

*Duke of York's Column*

Further up the Mall is Paul Day's **statue of Queen Elizabeth** (1900-2002), the Queen Mother, in front of her late husband King George VI. The bronze panels alongside depict events from her long life. Ahead of you, spanning the road is **Admiralty Arch**. Before this, look on the left for the (Grand Old) **Duke of York's column**, paid for by stopping a day's pay from every soldier in the British Army in 1827.

## I-SPY Tick List:

- **Queen Mother Statue** ○
- **Admiralty Arch** ○
- **Duke of York's Column** ○

# I-SPY The Mall

Climb the steps into **Carlton House Terrace** to spy the equestrian statue of **King Edward VII**. Surrounding him in the square are six statues. The one in the top right corner is of **Scott of the Antarctic**.

*Scott of the Antarctic*

*King Edward VII*

## I-SPY Tick List:

- **Carlton House Terrace** ◯
- **King Edward VII** ◯
- **Scott of the Antarctic** ◯
- **Lord John Lawrence** ◯
- **Field Marshall Lloyd Clyde** ◯
- **Field Marshall John Fox Burgoyne** ◯
- **Sir John Franklin** ◯
- **Sir Keith Park** ◯

*Athenaeum Club*

*Florence Nightingale and Guards' Crimean Memorial*

The large building on the left with the blue frieze is the **Athenaeum Club**. Ahead, across Pall Mall is the **Guards' Crimean Memorial** and **Florence Nightingale** statue. The guns behind the memorial were captured from the Russians at Sebastopol; the figures were cast from melted down Russian cannons.

## I-SPY Tick List:

- **Athenaeum Club** ○
- **Guards' Crimean Memorial** ○
- **Florence Nightingale** 

*King William III Statue in St James's Square*

## I-SPY Tick List:

- **King William III** ○
- **London Library** ○

Walking left down Pall Mall you will find a narrow street leading into St James's Square with it's statue of **King William III**. Look for the **London Library** in the far corner – it was founded by Thomas Carlyle in 1841.

*London Library*

*Nancy Astor*

Around St James's Square are some interesting blue plaques. No. 4 has a plaque to **Nancy Astor** the first woman to become a Member of Parliament. Back in Pall Mall are the former homes of the painter **Thomas Gainsborough**, **Napoleon III** and **Nell Gwyn** (spelt Gwynne on the plaque), the 17th-century actress who became mistress to Charles II.

*Thomas Gainsborough*

*Napoleon III*

*Nell Gwyn*

## I-SPY Tick List:

- **Nancy Astor** ○
- **Thomas Gainsborough** ○
- **Napoleon III** ○
- **Nell Gwyn** ○

# I-SPY Pall Mall

Berry Brothers and Rudd

At the bottom of Pall Mall is the gateway to St James's Palace. Charles I spent his last night here. The poet Byron had his lodgings in St James's Street which has many famous and long-established shops; **Berry Brothers and Rudd** (wine); **James Lock & Co** (hats); and **Lobb** (boots).

James Lock & Co

Lobb

 I-SPY Tick List:

- **Berry Brothers and Rudd** ○
- **James Lock & Co** ○
- **Lobb** ○

If you have time, detour into **St James's Place**. The composer and pianist, Frederic Chopin (1810-1849), left **No. 4** in 1848 to give his very last public performance. Further up St James's, turn right into Jermyn Street, which has a wonderful variety of traditional (and expensive) shops, many of them 'By Appointment' suppliers to Her Majesty the Queen and other members of the royal family. Many famous tailors are located here, including **Turnbull & Asser**. Your nose may lead you to **Floris** the perfumer, run by the same family since 1739. Equally exciting, but rather different, aromas come from the cheese shop **Paxton & Whitfield**.

## I-SPY Tick List:

- **St James's Place** ◯
- **No. 4 St James's Place** ◯
- **Turnbull & Asser** ◯
- **Floris** ◯
- **Paxton & Whitfield** ◯

*Turnbull & Asser*

*Floris*

*Paxton & Whitfield*

# Shepherd Market/Curzon Street

**Princes Arcade** will take you back into Piccadilly. Walk left, past Green Park turning up White Horse Street into **Shepherd Market**. This delightful maze of alleys was designed by the builder Edward Shepherd in 1735. Walk up to Curzon Street looking for **G. F. Trumper** where the aristocracy have been shaved and trimmed for generations.

*G. F. Trumper*

*Ye Grapes pub in Shepherd Market*

## I-SPY Tick List:

- **Princes Arcade** ○
- **Shepherd Market** ○
- **G. F. Trumper** 

# Berkeley Square/Bond Street

From Curzon Street, go up Fitzmaurice Place into **Berkeley Square**. On the right of the square is Bruton Street. Her Majesty the Queen was born on 21st April 1926 at **No. 17**, her maternal grandfathers house, but this was destroyed by a bomb in 1940.

Bruton Street leads to Bond Street where you will find many of London's exclusive shops including **Tiffany & Co** and **Asprey** the jewellers, fashion houses such as **Alexander McQueen** and **Sotheby's** the auction house.

*Asprey*

*Sotheby's*

*Tiffany & Co*

## I-SPY Tick List:

- **Berkeley Square** ○
- **No. 17 Bruton Street** ○
- **Tiffany & Co** ○
- **Asprey** ○
- **Alexander McQueen** ○
- **Sotheby's** ○

# Grosvenor Square/Hanover Square

From Bond Street you can walk down Brook Street past **Claridge's Hotel** to **Grosvenor Square** to see the **American Embassy** and the statues of **F. D. Roosevelt** and **Dwight Eisenhower**. In the top left corner is a rare example of a blue **police phone box**.

*Claridge's Hotel*

*F. D. Roosevelt*

*American Embassy*

## I-SPY Tick List:

- **Claridge's Hotel** ○
- **Grosvenor Square** ○
- **American Embassy** ○
- **F. D. Roosevelt** ○
- **Dwight Eisenhower** ○
- **Police Phone Box** ○

# Grosvenor Square/Hanover Square

Return to Brook Street and pass No. 67 where there is a wall plaque to **The Bee Gees** who composed many of their songs here between 1968-1980. Further on at **No. 25** the composer Handel (1685-1759) wrote all his major works including the Messiah. You will find a delightful **mural** dedicated to him in Lancaster Court.
Spanning musical generations, and on the same house, you'll find a plaque to guitar legend **Jimi Hendrix** (1942-1970). Opposite notice the strangely named **Haunch of Venison Yard**.
Before reaching Regent Street you will pass Hanover Square.
A statue to **William Pitt the Younger** (1759-1806) stands at the southern end. Pitt was Britain's youngest Prime Minister at the age of 24.

*Handel Mural at Lancaster Court*

*The Bee Gees*

*Jimi Hendrix*

## I-SPY Tick List:

- **The Bee Gees** ○
- **No. 25 Brook Street** ○
- **Handel Mural** ○
- **Jimi Hendrix** ○
- **Haunch of Venison Yard** ○
- **William Pitt the Younger** ○

#  Regent Street

Apple Store

Hamleys

**Regent Street** was designed by John Nash (between 1813 and 1825) as part of the grand carriageway connecting the Prince Regent's residence, Carlton House, with Regent's Park. Look out for landmarks such as **Garrard**, the Queen's jewellers, the ultra-modern **Apple Store** and the world famous **Hamleys** toy shop.

 I-SPY Tick List:

- **Regent Street** ○
- **Garrard** ○
- **Apple Store** ○
- **Hamleys** ○

# Carnaby Street/Berwick Street

**Liberty** is a wonderful store to wander around in. The Tudor building in Great Marlborough Street was only built in 1922-1924! From here, on your left, Argyll Street is home to the world famous **London Palladium**. On your right, is the iconic **Carnaby Street** the fashion capital of the 1960s. Halfway down, on the corner of Broadwick Street, you will find the colourful mural – the **Spirit of Soho**.

*Carnaby Street*

*London Palladium*

*Liberty*

## I-SPY Tick List:

- **Liberty** ○
- **London Palladium** ○
- **Carnaby Street** ○
- **Spirit of Soho** ○

# Carnaby Street/Berwick Street

Berwick Street Market

Further on, at the corner of Noel Street and Poland Street, is the house where the poet, **Percy Bysshe Shelley** (1792-1822) lived. Another poet, **William Blake** (1757-1827), lived in a house on the corner of Broadwick and Marshall Street. Broadwick Street is famous for **Berwick Street Market**.

Mary Shelley (1779-1851) the second wife of Percy Bysshe Shelley wrote the novel Frankenstein, published anonymously in London in 1818.

In the 19th century, Broadwick was known as Broad Street. In 1854 it was notorious as the centre of an outbreak of cholera. John Snow traced the outbreak of the disease to a public water pump. A replica pump is located close to the **John Snow pub**.

## I-SPY Tick List:

- **Percy Bysshe Shelley**
- **William Blake Plaque**
- **Berwick Street Market**
- **John Snow Pub**

You are now in the heart of Soho which can be pictured as the shape of a fork with four prongs: Wardour Street, Dean Street, Frith Street, and Greek Street, joined at the bottom by Old Compton Street. This probably makes **Soho Square** the green pea on the end of one prong! Standing proudly in Soho Square is a statue to **King Charles II** (1630-1685).

 I-SPY Tick List:

- **Soho Square** ○
- **King Charles II** ○

*King Charles II*

*Soho Square*

# Soho

Ronnie Scott's

**No. 163 Wardour Street** was the home of Thomas Sheraton (1751-1806), the furniture maker. **Dean Street** is where Karl Marx (1818-1883) began his writings on communism. **No 26 Frith Street** is famous for the world's first television demonstration by its inventor, the Scot, John Logie Baird (1888-1946) in 1926, and also for **Ronnie Scott's** Jazz Club. Look for the well-known **Gay Hussar** Hungarian restaurant in Greek Street.

Gay Hussar

## I-SPY Tick List:

- **No. 163 Wardour Street** ◯
- **Dean Street** ◯
- **No. 26 Frith Street** ◯
- **Ronnie Scott's** ◯
- **Gay Hussar** ◯

**Shaftesbury Avenue**, with its many theatres runs parallel to Old Compton Street. At the end of Shaftesbury Avenue, the **Palace Theatre** dominates Cambridge Circus. Below it, Gerrard Street is the heart of London's Chinatown. The present location of London's Chinatown was not established until the 1970s. The first was in the Limehouse area of the East End of London where the Chinese community was concentrated at the start of the 20th century.

I-SPY Tick List:

- **Shaftesbury Avenue** ○
- **Palace Theatre** ○

*Palace Theatre in Cambridge Circus*

# London's Theatres

I-SPY Tick List:

- Adelphi ○
- Aldwych ○
- Apollo ○
- Arts ○
- Cambridge ○
- Comedy ○
- Criterion ○
- Dominion ○
- Donmar Warehouse ○
- Duchess ○
- Duke of York's ○
- Fortune ○

- Garrick ○
- Gielgud ○
- Her Majesty's ○
- ICA ○
- Jermyn Street ○
- Leicester Square ○
- London Coliseum ○

- London Palladium ○
- Lyceum ○
- Lyric ○
- New Ambassadors ○
- New London ○
- Noel Coward ○
- Novello ○
- Palace ○
- Peacock ○
- Phoenix ○
- Piccadilly ○
- Player's ○
- Playhouse ○
- Prince Edward ○
- Prince of Wales ○
- Queen's ○
- Royal Opera House ○
- St Martin's ○
- Savoy ○
- Shaftesbury ○
- Soho ○
- Theatre Royal - Drury Lane ○
- Theatre Royal - Haymarket ○
- Trafalgar Studios ○
- Vaudeville ○
- Venue, The ○
- Wyndham's ○

# I-SPY Trafalgar Square

**Trafalgar Square**, named after Admiral Nelson's great naval victory over the Spanish and French fleets in 1805, is dominated by **Nelson's Column**, 56m (185ft) high. The battle scenes at its base were cast from captured French cannons, and the **Lions** from cannons of the Royal George ship which sank in 1782.

*Trafalgar Square Lion*

## I-SPY Tick List:

- **Trafalgar Square** ○
- **Nelson's Column** ○
- **Lions** ○

*Trafalgar Square and Nelson's Column*

# Trafalgar Square

National Gallery

To the north of the Square is the **National Gallery** which houses one of the greatest collections of paintings in the world. Next door is the **National Portrait Gallery**. To your left is the church of **St Martin-in-the-Fields**, where King Charles II was baptized and his mistress, Nell Gwyn, buried. South, across Trafalgar Square, you can see down Whitehall to the Houses of Parliament and Big Ben.

St Martin-in-the-Fields

## I-SPY Tick List:

- **National Gallery** ○
- **National Portrait Gallery** ○
- **St Martin-in-the-Fields** ○

# Charing Cross

Charing Cross

Before that, at the south east side of the Square, is the central point for measuring distances from London, **Charing Cross**. When you see a sign 'London 55 miles' – it is to this point.

**Whitehall** takes its name from Henry VIII's royal palace in which he married Anne Boleyn and where he died in 1547.

Charing Cross denotes the junction of the Strand, Whitehall and Cockspur Street just the south of Trafalgar Square. It is named after the long-ago demolished Eleanor cross (now occupied by the statue of Charles I on his horse) in the hamlet of Charing.

## I-SPY Tick List:

- **Charing Cross**
- **Whitehall**

# Whitehall I-SPY

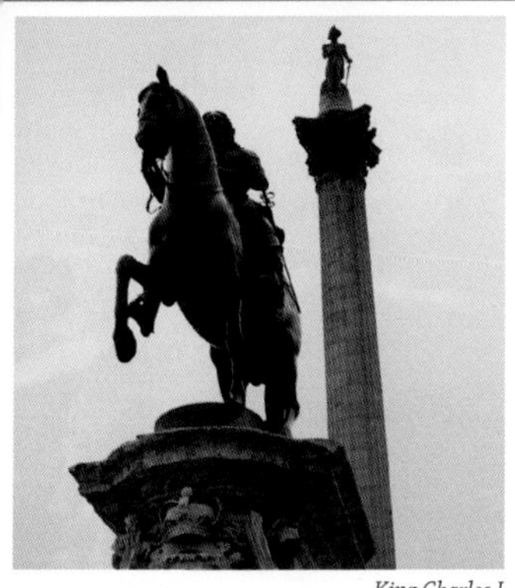

*King Charles I*

An equestrian statue of **King Charles I** looks wistfully down Whitehall to where he was beheaded in 1649. In Whitehall you will see the huge **Old War Office** building, now part of the Ministry of Defence. Opposite is **Horse Guards** with its clock tower and guard mounted by the Household Cavalry.

## I-SPY Tick List:

- **King Charles I** ○
- **Old War Office** ○
- **Horse Guards** ○

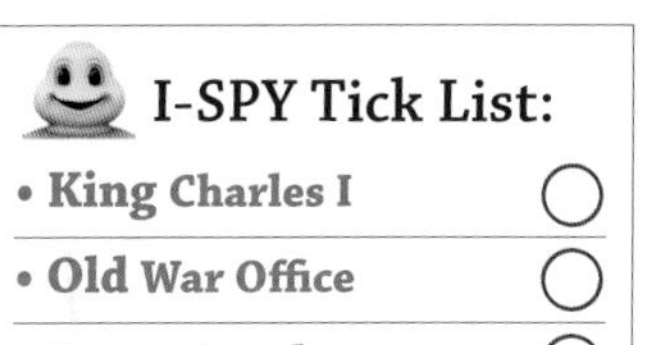

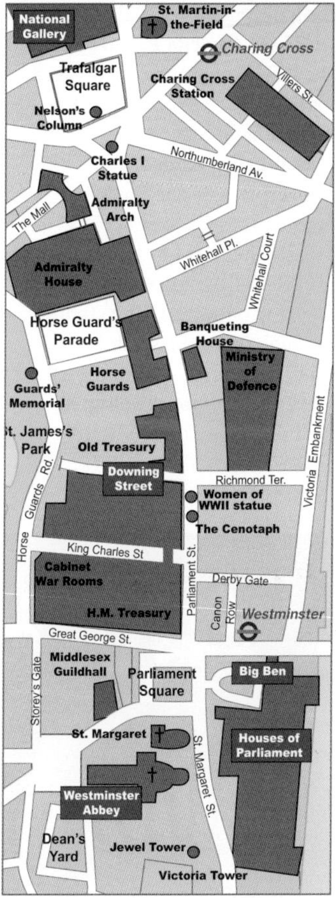

Back on Whitehall, walk through to **Horse Guards Parade** where the trooping of the colour takes place.

Take time to look at the **Banqueting House**, a masterpiece by the English architect, Inigo Jones (1573-1652). The bust of Charles I (1600-1649) marks the position of the window the King stepped through on to the scaffold in 1649; Charles I of whom it is said 'never said a foolish thing, nor ever did a wise one'.

## I-SPY Tick List:

- **Horse Guards Parade** 
- **Banqueting House**

*Horse Guards Parade*

In the centre of Whitehall are two war memorials. The first is the 2005 National Monument to **Women of World War II**. The next is the **Cenotaph**, the country's official war memorial, commemorating servicemen and women who died in the two World Wars. Just up on the right, now protected by secure railings is **Downing Street**. No. 10 is the home of the Prime Minister.

*Women of World War II*

## I-SPY Tick List:

- **The Cenotaph** ○
- **Women of World War II** ○
- **Downing Street** ○

*Cenotaph*

*Corner of Downing Street and Whitehall*

# St James's Park/Downing Street

Nearby is the **Churchill Museum** and **Cabinet War Rooms** and beyond them **St James's Park**, London's oldest park. Along its southern side is **Birdcage Walk** named after Charles II's aviary.

*Cabinet War Rooms*

## I-SPY Tick List:

- **Churchill Museum** ○
- **Cabinet War Rooms** ○
- **St James's Park** ○
- **Birdcage Walk** ○

*St James's Park*

# Houses of Parliament

Before entering Parliament Square, walk out on to **Westminster Bridge** for one of the best views of the **Houses of Parliament**. Its proper title 'Palace of Westminster' comes from the fact that this was the site of the sovereign's main London residence from Saxon times until 1529 when Henry VIII took Whitehall from Cardinal Wolsey. The present building was opened by Queen Victoria in 1852.

## I-SPY Tick List:

- **Westminster Bridge**
- **Houses of Parliament** 

*Westminster Bridge and Houses of Parliament*

# Houses of Parliament

Big Ben

The Victoria Tower is the tallest stone square tower in the world at over 102 meters (336ft), although the Clock Tower is more famous. **Big Ben**, as the Clock Tower is often known, is really the 13 ½ -ton bell cast at the Whitechapel Bell Foundry of Mears and Stainbank. It is Big Ben's chime which marks the passing of the hours in London.

Walk along Victoria Embankment, away from Big Ben to the **Battle of Britain Monument** which pays tribute to those who took part in the World War II battle.

Battle of Britain Monument

## I-SPY Tick List:

- **Big Ben** ○
- **Battle of Britain Monument** 

# Parliament Square

Returning to Parliament Square you will pass the statue of **Boudicca** (Boadicea) driving her own answer to London's traffic. **Sir Winston Churchill** (1874-1965) dominates the green much as he did the Commons in his lifetime, but there are many other interesting statues. On the far side is **Middlesex Guildhall**, to the left **St Margaret's Church** with its pale blue sundial clocks.

I-SPY Tick List:

- **Boudicca** ○
- **Sir Winston Churchill** ○
- **Middlesex Guildhall** ○
- **St Margaret's Church** ○

*Boudicca*

*Sir Winston Churchill*

# Westminster Abbey

No building has more to tell of English history than **Westminster Abbey**. It has seen the coronation of every monarch since William the Conqueror and contains memorials to many of the nation's great men and women. The first recorded church on the site was built before AD 750 but the present structure is medieval. The nave was built in the late fourteenth century by the mysterious architect Henry Yevele.

The most important addition since then was **Henry VII's Chapel**. Of all the Abbey's numerous memorials, the most moving is the grave of the **Unknown Warrior**. Truly unknown, he was buried with the highest honours in 1921 and lies in soil brought from the battlefield: an anonymous representative of more than a million men who gave their lives in World War I.

Westminster Abbey was seen by millions around the world when Prince William and Catherine Middleton married on 29th April 2011.

*Westminster Abbey*

## I-SPY Tick List:

- **Westminster Abbey** ○
- **Henry VII's Chapel** ○
- **Unknown Warrior** ○

Outside again, return to Cromwell Green where a bronze statue of **Oliver Cromwell** (1599-1658) presides over the Parliament he gave life to. On the same spot Guy Fawkes (1570-1606) and other Gunpowder Plot conspirators were executed following their failed attempt to blow up the Houses of Parliament. This failure is celebrated every November 5th. A little further and you will find a statue to **King Richard I** (Richard the Lionheart (1157-1199).

*Oliver Cromwell*

*King Richard I*

## I-SPY Tick List:

- **Oliver Cromwell** ○
- **King Richard I** 

# I-SPY Palace Yard/Victoria Tower Gardens

*Emmeline Pankhurst*

*Burghers of Calais*

**Victoria Tower Gardens** are interesting. There is a statue of **Emmeline Pankhurst** (1858-1928), who fought for women's rights, and a reproduction of the statue by Rodin of the heroic **Burghers of Calais**, as well as the colourful **Buxton Memorial Fountain**.

I-SPY Tick List:

- **Victoria Tower Gardens** ○
- **Emmeline Pankhurst** ○
- **Burghers of Calais** ○
- **Buxton Memorial Fountain** ○

# Westminster Cathedral

From Parliament Square a long walk or a short bus ride down Victoria Street will bring you to **Westminster Cathedral**, England's principal Roman Catholic Church, consecrated in 1910. From the bell tower (campanile) there are wonderful views of London. On a clear day it is possible to see the North Downs and Crystal Palace to the south and Harrow and Hampstead to the north. The campanile is 83 metres (273ft) high, but there is a lift!

## I-SPY Tick List:

- **Westminster Cathedral** ○

*Westminster Cathedral*

A shorter route, passing the Houses of Parliament, takes you to the statue of **King George V** (1865-1936). In front of him, on the floor, is the **Human Sundial**, commemorating the Golden Jubilee of Queen Elizabeth II in 2002. Next is the **Jewel Tower**, built in 1365 to house the treasures of King Edward III. Together with Westminster Hall these are the only two surviving sections of the medieval Palace of Westminster.

*King George V*

*Jewel Tower*

## I-SPY Tick List:

- **King George V** ○
- **Human Sundial** ○
- **Jewel Tower** ○

*Lambeth Bridge*

*Tate Britain*

Walk down Millbank passing **Lambeth Bridge**. On the right is the **Tate Britain**, built by sugar magnate Sir Henry Tate. The gallery houses a magnificent collection of modern paintings and sculpture. Inside, amongst many fine paintings, look for **Rodin's *The Kiss***.

## I-SPY Tick List:

- **Lambeth Bridge** ○
- **Tate Britain** ○
- **Rodin's *The Kiss*** ○

*Harrods at Christmas*

Start at Knightsbridge Underground station. Immediately in front of you is probably the world's most famous store, **Harrods**. Walk down Beauchamp Place (pronounced Beecham) and take a detour along Walton Street (author P. G. Wodehouse lived at **No. 16**) to the wonderful art deco **Michelin House**, former UK headquarters of Michelin Tyre PLC in Fulham Road, opened in 1911, with its stained glass windows of the Michelin man.

*Michelin House*

## I-SPY Tick List:

- **Harrods** ○
- **No. 16 Walton Street** ○
- **Michelin House** ○

Returning to Beauchamp Place and Pont Street, cross Sloane Street with its smart shops, down Chesham Place into **Belgrave Square**. Here you will find the signature of George Basevi on No. 37. He was the architect employed by Thomas Cubitt to design most of the fine squares in this most fashionable area of London. In the centre is a statue of **Christopher Columbus** (1451-1506).

South of Belgrave Square and Eaton Square is Chester Square. Mary Shelley, author of Frankenstein, died at **No. 24**. Ebury Street, further down Eccleston Street is full of interest. At the age of 8, the Austrian composer, Wolfgang Amadeus **Mozart** (1756-91) completed his first symphony at No. 180.

*Christopher Columbus in Belgrave Square*

*Mozart*

## I-SPY Tick List:

- **Belgrave Square**
- **Christopher Columbus**
- **No. 24 Chester Square**
- **Mozart**

# Belgrava/Harrods

From Chester Square, walk toward Sloane Square where you find the **Royal Court Theatre**. Chelsea's fashionable King's Road lies ahead of you with its huge selection of trendy designer shops.

*Little Ben*

From Victoria Station, turn left and spot the clock tower, **Little Ben**. Walk down Buckingham Palace Road to **Chelsea Bridge**. Across the Thames is the redundant **Battersea Power Station** (nicknamed the 'inverted grand piano').

## I-SPY Tick List:

- **Royal Court Theatre** ○
- **Little Ben** ○
- **Chelsea Bridge** ○
- **Battersea Power Station** ○

*Battersea Power Station*

From Chelsea Bridge, go up Chelsea Bridge Road and turn left into Royal Hospital Road. On the top corner of Burton's Court, in St Leonard's Terrace, is an original 1872 hexagonal **'penfold' letterbox**. To your left are the grounds of the **Royal Hospital** where the Chelsea Flower Show is held each year. Sir Christopher Wren (1632-1723) was the architect of the Royal (or Chelsea) Hospital which was founded by Charles III in 1682 for veteran and invalid soldiers. Further on you will come to the **National Army Museum**. Turn left into Tite Street and turn right into Dilke Street, along to Swan Walk and the **Chelsea Physic Garden**. This ancient apothecaries' garden is sometimes open to the public. Even if it is not, peer through the gates and reflect that the very first cotton seeds were taken from this little garden to America in 1732.

*National Army Museum*

*Penfold Letterbox*

## I-SPY Tick List:

- **Penfold Letterbox** ○
- **Royal Hospital** ○
- **National Army Museum** ○
- **Chelsea Physic Garden** ○

# Cheyne Walk

On the riverside there is an interesting monument to **Sir Joseph William Bazalgette** (1819-1891), the engineer of the Chelsea Embankment who also constructed the main sewage system of London. Nearby, and close to the site of his former house, is a statue of **Sir Thomas More** (1478-1535), the former Lord Chancellor, who was martyred by Henry VIII. Towards the end of Cheyne Walk is **No. 119**, where the artist, Joseph Turner died in 1851; curiously, although it was a foggy December morning, it is recorded that a shaft of sunlight flooded his little attic room at the moment of his death.

*Sir Thomas More*

*Sir Joseph William Bazalgette*

## I-SPY Tick List:

- **Sir Joseph William Bazalgette** ○
- **Sir Thomas More** ○
- **No. 119 Cheyne Walk** ○

# Hyde Park Corner

**Hyde Park Corner** is one of the busiest junctions in London so take extra care and use the pedestrian subway to cross. This military place has memorials to the **Royal Artillery**, the **Machine Gun Corps** and the **New Zealand War Memorial**, but the dominating presence is of the **'Iron Duke' of Wellington** (1769- 1852).

I-SPY Tick List:

- **Hyde Park Corner** ○
- **Royal Artillery Memorial** ○
- **Machine Gun Corps Memorial** ○
- **New Zealand War Memorial** ○
- **'Iron Duke' of Wellington** ○

*Royal Artillery Memorial*

*Machine Gun Corps Memorial*

# I-SPY Hyde Park Corner

*Wellington Arch*

The Constitution or **Wellington Arch** at the centre, was erected in 1828, and there is a statue of the Duke mounted on his war horse, Copenhagen, in front of **Apsley House** (known as No. 1 London) which was his London home for many years.

 I-SPY Tick List:

- **Wellington Arch** 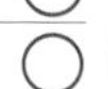
- **Apsley House**

*Apsley House*

Close to the entrance to Hyde Park, behind the magnificent Queen Elizabeth Gates looms the **Wellington Monument**. It shows Achilles, the legendary Greek figure made from melted-down French cannons and dedicated by 'their countrywomen' to Wellington and his soldiers. Three paths lead into Hyde Park (from right to left) Serpentine Road, sandy Rotten Row (from the French Route du Roi - 'King's Way') for riders, and the Carriageway which can be taken for Knightsbridge. From Apsley House, take the Serpentine Road (once called Ladies' Mile) stopping, if you have time for refreshments at the **Serpentine Bar and Kitchen** to the man-made lake, **The Serpentine**. To your right was the site of the Great Exhibition of 1851. Follow the path or make you own way round to Marble Arch at the top of Park Lane.

*Wellington Monument*

*Serpentine Bar and Kitchen*

## I-SPY Tick List:

- **Wellington Monument** ○
- **Serpentine Bar and Kitchen** ○
- **The Serpentine** ○

# Hyde Park/Kensington Gardens

## I-SPY Tick List:

- Queen Victoria Statue ○
- Physical Energy ○
- Peter Pan ○
- Fountain ○
- Italian Garden ○
- Round Pond ○
- Boats ○

# Hyde Park/Kensington Gardens

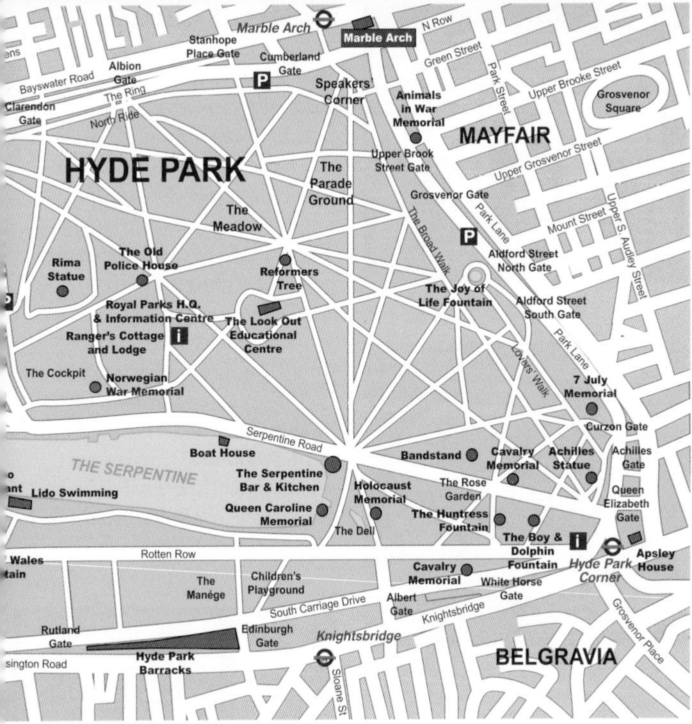

- **Albert Memorial** ◯
- **Bandstand** ◯
- **Horse Riders** ◯
- **Roller Bladers** ◯

- **Ducks and Swans** ◯
- **Deck Chairs** ◯
- **Picnickers** ◯
- **Frisbee** ◯

# I-SPY Marble Arch

Marble Arch

**Marble Arch** was originally built as the main gate to Buckingham Palace but, because it proved to be too narrow for the King's Coach, it was moved. Its present site has a ghastly history. This was Tyburn, for 600 years London's public execution place. The position of the permanent gallows, **'Tyburn Tree'**, is marked by a stone on the island opposite Edgware Road. Countless men and women – highwaymen and priests, the good and the bad – were hanged here. **Speakers' Corner**, just inside Hyde Park is often busy with public speakers, especially on Sunday mornings.

Tyburn Tree

## I-SPY Tick List:

- **Marble Arch** ○
- **Tyburn Tree** ○
- **Speakers' Corner** ○

Speakers' Corner

You can now detour and explore the northern side of the park or walk down Park Lane. In the middle of the road, where it meets Upper Grosvenor Street, is a memorial to **Animals in War**. Unveiled in 2004, the 90th anniversary of the start of World War I, it is a tribute to all animals that suffered in the conflicts of the 20th century.

Most of the original great mansions along Park Lane are now gone or have been replaced by grand hotels. Look for **The Dorchester** and the **London Hilton** before returning to Hyde Park Corner.

## I-SPY Tick List:

- **Animals in War Memorial** ○
- **The Dorchester** ○
- **London Hilton** ○

*The Dorchester*

*London Hilton*

# I-SPY Brompton Oratory

*Victoria and Albert Museum*

Although several of London's major museums are close together, it is a mistake to try to see too much at once. It is an interesting part of town so you can add variety to each visit. Start from South Kensington Underground and walk up Thurloe Place. Just past the **Ismaili Centre**, built by the Aga Khan Foundation, the road joins Cromwell Gardens.
In front of you will be the **Victoria and Albert Museum** which houses an incomparable collection of art and decoration from all countries and periods.

Next to the Victoria and Albert Museum is the **Brompton Oratory**, a famous Roman Catholic Church. Look for the statue of **Cardinal Newman** behind some iron railings.

## I-SPY Tick List:

- **Ismaili Centre** ○
- **Victoria and Albert Museum** ○
- **Brompton Oratory** ○
- **Cardinal Newman** ○

# Exhibition Road

Retrace your steps to the Victoria and Albert and you will see in the middle of the road one of the few remaining **Cabmen's Shelters** used by London's taxi drivers for many years and now preserved. Cross Exhibition Road and you will come to the **Natural History Museum** with its unrivalled archive of specimens and, of course, its dinosaurs. Just past the museum is **Baden-Powell House**, built as a tribute to Lord Baden-Powell, the founder of the Scout Movement.

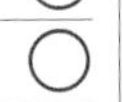

## I-SPY Tick List:

- **Cabmen's Shelter** ○
- **Natural History Museum** ○
- **Baden-Powell House** ○

*Cabmen's Shelter*

*Natural History Museum*

# I-SPY Exhibition Road

On the south side of Cromwell Road is the **French Lycée**. Return to, and turn up Exhibition Road to reach the **Science Museum**, full of wonderful exhibits and hands-on interactive displays. Further up, look for the **Royal College of Music** to the left in Prince Consort Road. At the top of Exhibition Road, you may find the British Antarctic explorer, **Sir Ernest Shackleton** (1874-1922), sheltering in an alcove in the wall of the Royal Geographical Society, with missionary **David Livingstone** (1813-1873) for company. Look out here, too, for an interesting cast iron **mile post** set on the wall.

## I-SPY Tick List:

- **French Lycée** ○
- **Science Museum** ○
- **Royal College of Music** ○
- **Sir Ernest Shackleton** ○
- **David Livingstone** ○
- **Cast Iron Mile Post** ○

*Sir Ernest Shackleton*

*Science Museum*

# Royal Albert Hall I-SPY

Royal Albert Hall

Turning left into Kensington Gore, you will see the **Royal Albert Hall**. This is where the famous Promenade Concerts ('the Proms') begun by Sir Henry Wood (1869-1944) are held each year. Opposite the Royal Albert Hall, is the **Albert Memorial**: the controversial golden monument Queen Victoria had built after the death of her beloved consort Prince Albert (1819-1861). If you look closely, you will see that the Prince is holding the catalogue of the Great Exhibition of 1851.

Albert Memorial

## I-SPY Tick List:

- **Royal Albert Hall** ○
- **Albert Memorial** ○

*Kensington Gardens*

*Peter Pan*

**Kensington Gardens** is quite different in mood from Hyde Park. This is the magical world of **Peter Pan** and you will find the statue of J. M. Barrie's character, the boy who remains eternally young, by the Long Water.

I-SPY Tick List:

- **Kensington Gardens** ○
- **Peter Pan** ○

Make your way to the edge of the Gardens where you can glimpse Wren's **Kensington Palace** and the **Orangery**. Queen Victoria was born in Kensington Palace in 1819 and lived there until she ascended the throne in 1827. The State Apartments and magnificent Court Dress Collection are well worth seeing before leaving the Gardens.

## I-SPY Tick List:

- **Kensington Palace**
- **Orangery**

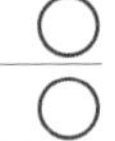

*Kensington Palace*

# I-SPY River Thames

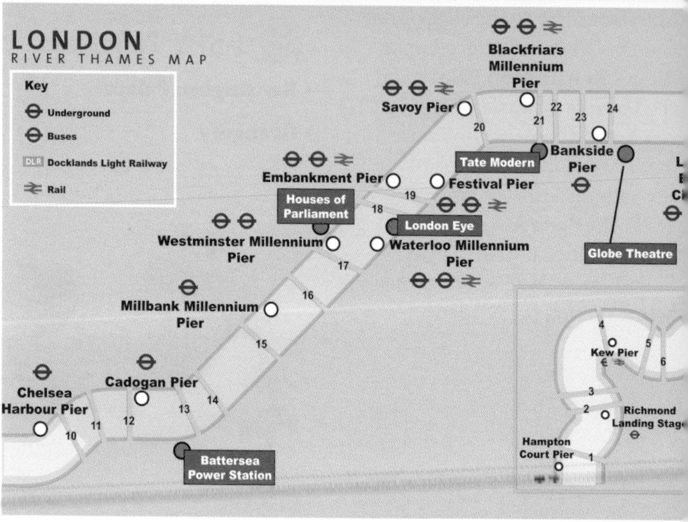
LONDON
RIVER THAMES MAP
Key
Underground
Buses
DLR Docklands Light Railway
Rail
Blackfriars Millennium Pier
Savoy Pier
Tate Modern
Bankside Pier
Embankment Pier
Festival Pier
Houses of Parliament
London Eye
Westminster Millennium Pier
Waterloo Millennium Pier
Globe Theatre
Millbank Millennium Pier
Cadogan Pier
Chelsea Harbour Pier
Battersea Power Station
Kew Pier
Richmond Landing Stage
Hampton Court Pier
1
2
3
4
5
6
10
11
12
13
14
15
16
17
18
19
20
21
22
23
24

## I-SPY Tick List:

- Duck Tour
- Police Launch
- River Taxi
- RNLI
- Clipper

Beatrice

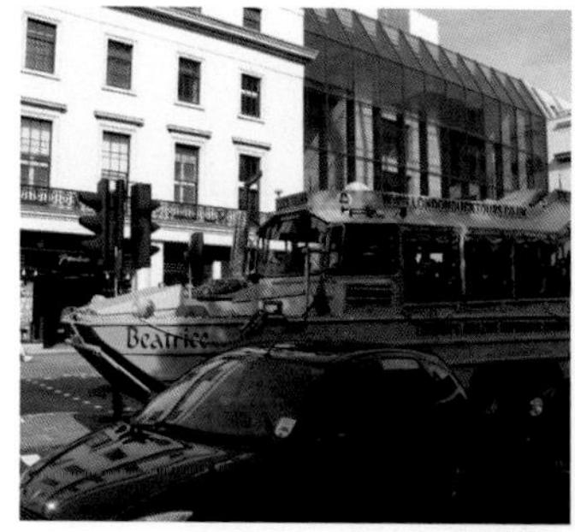

*Duck Tour*

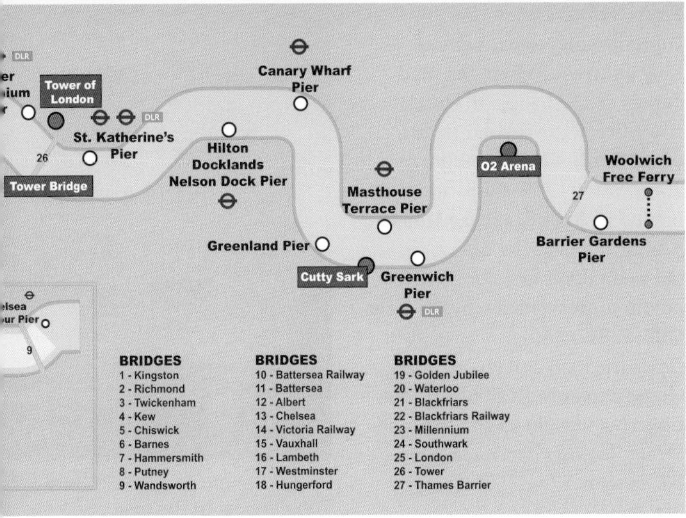

Tower of London

St. Katherine's Pier

Tower Bridge

Canary Wharf Pier

Hilton Docklands Nelson Dock Pier

Masthouse Terrace Pier

Greenland Pier

Cutty Sark

Greenwich Pier

O2 Arena

Woolwich Free Ferry

Barrier Gardens Pier

**BRIDGES**
1 - Kingston
2 - Richmond
3 - Twickenham
4 - Kew
5 - Chiswick
6 - Barnes
7 - Hammersmith
8 - Putney
9 - Wandsworth

**BRIDGES**
10 - Battersea Railway
11 - Battersea
12 - Albert
13 - Chelsea
14 - Victoria Railway
15 - Vauxhall
16 - Lambeth
17 - Westminster
18 - Hungerford

**BRIDGES**
19 - Golden Jubilee
20 - Waterloo
21 - Blackfriars
22 - Blackfriars Railway
23 - Millennium
24 - Southwark
25 - London
26 - Tower
27 - Thames Barrier

*Restaurant Boat*

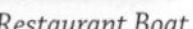

# I-SPY Fitzrovia

From Oxford Circus Underground, walk north up Regent Street. Where the road curves at The Langham Hotel, you will see the circular front of **All Souls Church** built by John Nash (1752-1835) and, behind it, **Broadcasting House**, headquarters of the BBC. Over the main door, look for the frieze by the controversial sculptor **Eric Gill** (1882-1940).

Cross the road and go up Riding House Street in front of All Souls Church and walk up to Cleveland Street, looking north for the **BT Tower**, 177m (580ft) high, completed in 1964.

Broadcasting House

You are now in the heart of Fitzrovia which is full of interest, both for the people who have lived there and for the story its street names tell.

BT Tower

## I-SPY Tick List:

- **All Souls Church** ○
- **Broadcasting House** ○
- **Eric Gill Frieze** ○
- **BT Tower** ○

No. 22 Cleveland Street

The Duchess of Cleveland (born Barbara Villiers 1641-1709) had several children by Charles II: all these were called 'Fitzroy'. One son, Henry, was made Earl of Euston and then Duke of Grafton. He acquired by marriage a huge estate in the area around Tottenham Court Road which was developed much as you see it today.
Charles Dickens (1812-70) lived at **No. 22** Cleveland Street in 1830, and the painters Rossetti, Holman Hunt, and Millais founded the Pre-Raphaelite Brotherhood at **No. 7** in 1848.
At the bottom end of Cleveland Street turn into Tottenham Street and cross into Charlotte Street, now famous for its restaurants and once the home of the painter John Constable (1776-1837) at **No. 95**. A short detour down Scala Street to see **Pollock's Toy Museum** is well worthwhile.

Pollock's Toy Museum

## I-SPY Tick List:

- **No. 22 Cleveland Street** ○
- **No. 7 Cleveland Street** ○
- **No. 95 Charlotte Street** ○
- **Pollock's Toy Museum** ○

# Euston

*Euston Station*

From its junction with Goodge Street, walk northwards up Charlotte Street until you come to Fitzroy Square. Author George Bernard Shaw (1856-1950) lived here with his mother at **No. 29**; the novelist, Virginia Woolf (1882-1941), lived with her brother in the same house later. From Fitzroy Square, go north into Euston Road and turn right to see three of London's great stations. You will see **Euston** first. Look for the statue of the railway engineer **Robert Stephenson** (1803-1859) in the forecourt, and **Friends House**, the headquarters of the Quakers, in Euston Square.

*Robert Stephenson*

## I-SPY Tick List:

- **No. 29 Fitzroy Square** ○
- **Euston Station** ○
- **Robert Stephenson** ○
- **Friends House** ○

# St Pancras/King's Cross

*Eurostar at St Pancras Station*

On the left is the impressive structure of the **British Library**, the national library of the United Kingdom. It is one of the world's largest libraries with over 14 million books, 920,000 journals and newspaper titles and over 59 million patents!

Continue east along Euston Road until you see the romantic and extravagant structure of **St Pancras International** railway station. Originally opened in 1868 it escaped demolition in the 1960s and was magnificently restored and expanded during the 2000s at a cost of £800 million to connect the Eurostar service with Continental Europe.

*British Library*

## I-SPY Tick List:

- **British Library**
- **St Pancras International Station**
- **Eurostar Train**

# Portland Place/Harley Street

Adjacent to St Pancreas is the functional **King's Cross Station**, another example, although somewhat less grand, of Victorian architecture. The whole area of King's Cross was named after a monument to King George IV which was demolished in 1845. The **King's Cross Clock** was taken from the original Crystal Palace of the Great Exhibition of 1851. From King's Cross you can use the Underground to return to Oxford Circus.

From Oxford Circus, walk northwards up Regent Street, past the BBC into Portland Place. The novelist and crime writer, Edgar Wallace (1875-1932) lived at **No. 31**. Look for the statue of the famous surgeon Lord Lister (1827-1912) and his home at **No. 12** Park Crescent. Lister was the first person to use antiseptics in surgery to control infections.

*King's Cross Station*

*Park Crescent*

## I-SPY Tick List:

- **King's Cross Station** ○
- **King's Cross Clock** ○
- **No. 31 Portland Place** ○
- **No. 12 Park Crescent** ○

# Harley Street

On the corner of Park Crescent is a bust of assassinated US President **John F. Kennedy** (1917-1963). Turn left into Marylebone Road. Almost immediately on your left you will see Harley Street where many of Britain's finest doctors have consulting rooms.
If you feel like a detour, the British statesman W. E. Gladstone (1809-1898) lived at **No. 73**; the painter J M W Turner (1775-1851) lived at **No. 45** at the height of his popularity and from **No. 11** plain Sir Arthur Wellesley (later Duke of Wellington) left to find fame and fortune in the Peninsular War (1808-14).
Back in Marylebone Road, you will soon come to **Madame Tussaud's** waxworks exhibition and the Stardome.

## I-SPY Tick List:

- **John F. Kennedy** ○
- **No. 73 Harley Street** ○
- **No. 45 Harley Street** ○
- **No. 11 Harley Street** ○
- **Madame Tussaud's** ○

*John F. Kennedy*

*Madame Tussaud's*

# Regent's Park

*Regent's Park*

Just before York Gate, the way into **Regent's Park**, you must decide how to explore the Park and in what order.

*London Zoo*

Going left round the Outer Circle will take you past Hanover Terrace where Charles Dickens wrote *Great Expectations* at **No. 3** and where the English science fiction novelist, H. G. Wells (1866- 1946), lived at **No. 13**, on to the **London Central Mosque**, and finally to the **London Zoo**.

## I-SPY Tick List:

- **Regent's Park**
- **No. 3 Hanover Terrace**
- **No. 13 Hanover Terrace**
- **London Central Mosque**
- **London Zoo**

*Cumberland Terrace*

*Open Air Theatre*

*Pleasure Boats on Regent's Canal*

After that the Outer Circle returns past Nash's **Cumberland Terrace** to the top of Great Portland Street and to where you began at Oxford Circus. But, if you go straight on from York Gate, you will come to the Inner Circle with **Queen Mary's Gardens** and the **Open Air Theatre**. You can also take a **pleasure boat** on the Regent's Canal to Little Venice and Paddington.

## I-SPY Tick List:

- **Cumberland Terrace** ○
- **Queen Mary's Gardens** ○
- **Open Air Theatre** ○
- **Pleasure Boats** ○

# Little Venice

Start at **Paddington Station,** which is the terminus of Isambard Kingdom Brunel's (1806-1859) Great Western Railway. In Praed Street, you may like to see **St Mary's Hospital** where **Sir Alexander Fleming** (1881-1955) discovered penicillin. This was where both Prince William and Prince Harry were born. From Edgware Road, which was the Roman Watling Street, walk (or bus) down to the end of Seymour Street just before Marble Arch.

Paddington Station

Sir Alexander Fleming

Little Venice

## I-SPY Tick List:

- **Paddington Station** ○
- **Little Venice** ○
- **St Mary's Hospital** ○
- **Sir Alexander Fleming** ○

Edward Lear (1812-88), inventor of the nonsense limerick, lived at **No. 30** Seymour Street. To the north, and parallel, is George Street where – at **No. 5** Bryanston Court – King Edward VIII and Mrs Simpson used to meet. Keep walking eastwards until you come to Baker Street. At the north end, the house Sir Arthur Conan Doyle (1859-1930) chose for his fictional detective is **221b Baker Street**, now a popular museum for fans of the super-sleuth.

Go down Baker Street into Oxford Street to find the department store, **Selfridges**, first opened in 1909 by Harry Gordon Selfridge (1864-1947) who is credited with the phrase 'only .... shopping days until Christmas' as well as possibly coining the phrase 'the customer is always right'.

*'221b' Baker Street*

*Selfridges*

## I-SPY Tick List:

- **No. 30 Seymour Street** ○
- **No. 5 Bryanston Court** ○
- **No. 221b Baker Street** ○
- **Selfridges** ○

# Wimpole Street

Wallace Collection

Wigmore Hall

A detour up Duke Street into Manchester Square takes you to the **Wallace Collection**, perhaps the finest art collection ever donated by a private individual. Leave Manchester Square the way you entered and turn left along Wigmore Street past **Wigmore Hall**.

On your way to Regent Street and Oxford Circus, take time to walk up Wimpole Street. At **No. 50** (now rebuilt) lived the Barretts. Of the poet Robert Browning (1812-1889), whom she married, the daughter of the house, Elizabeth, was later to write '*How do I love thee? Let me count the ways* . . .'. They eloped on 20 September 1846.

I-SPY Tick List:

- **Wallace Collection** ○
- **Wigmore Hall** ○
- **No. 50 Wimpole Street** ○

# British Museum I-SPY

Start at Tottenham Court Road Underground. Go down Charing Cross Road. At 113-119 is the world famous bookshop, **Foyles**, selling books here since 1906. Further down on the left is the **Phoenix Theatre**. Follow the narrow alley to **St Giles-in the-Fields**. From here walk up St Giles High Street and turn right into New Oxford Street. Carry on past **James Smith & Sons**, the stick and umbrella shop established in 1830 and into Bloomsbury Way. Just past Museum Street is the **British Museum**, the most comprehensive and richest collection of its kind in the world. Leave the Museum and walk to Little Russell Street. At No. 35 is **The Cartoon Museum**, with its collections of illustrations, drawings and cartoons. Return to Bloomsbury and on to **Bedford Square** once famous for its publishers.

*British Museum*

## I-SPY Tick List:

- **Foyles** ○
- **Phoenix Theatre** ○
- **St Giles-in-the-Fields** ○
- **James Smith & Sons** ○
- **British Museum** ○
- **The Cartoon Museum** ○
- **Bedford Square** ○

# Coram's Fields

Turn right along Montague Place which leads up to Russell Square. On the east side is the **Russell Hotel**. Look for **No. 8** – the Pankhursts, who fought for women's rights, lived here then go along Guildford Street. On the left you will soon see **Coram's Fields** where Thomas Coram, with help from the composer Handel and Hogarth the painter, created the London Foundling Hospital to care for children. Leave the square at the southern end down Lamb's Conduit Street, past the famous **Lamb pub** and into Great Ormond Street. The world famous **children's hospital** is here.

Back up on Coram's Fields, Guilford Street crosses Doughty Street. Turn right down Doughty Street to find No. 48, the only surviving home of, and now **The Charles Dickens Museum**.

*Lamb Pub*

*The Charles Dickens Museum*

## I-SPY Tick List:

- **Russell Hotel** ○
- **No. 8 Russell Square** ○
- **Coram's Fields** ○
- **Lamb Pub** ○
- **Great Ormond Street Hospital** ○
- **The Charles Dickens Museum** ○

# Hatton Garden/Lincoln's Inn

Parallel to Doughty Street is the Gray's Inn Road. Turn right down here and all the way down to High Holburn. Take the second left and explore **Leather Lane Market**, and **Hatton Garden** which is the next turning. This is the London centre of the diamond business. Look for **Ye Olde Mitre** public house, first established in 1546. Back down to High Holborn the opposite way, just past Chancery Lane on the left is **Lincoln's Inn**, one of London's four Inns of Court. Every barrister in England and Wales must belong to Inner or Middle Temple, Gray's or Lincoln's Inn, to be able to practise law.

*Ye Olde Mitre Pub*

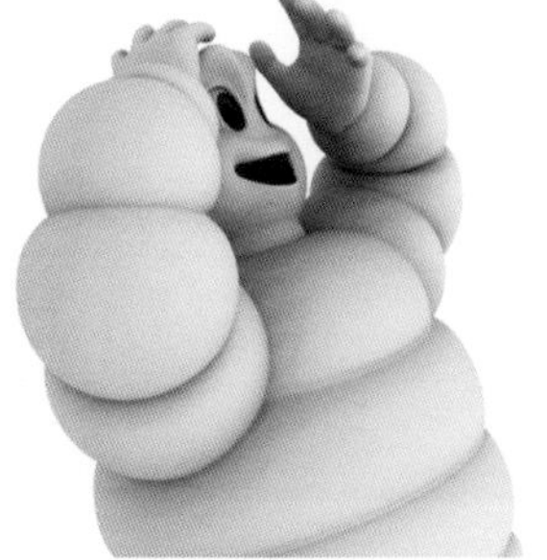

I-SPY Tick List:

- **Leather Lane Market** ○
- **Hatton Garden** ○
- **Ye Olde Mitre Pub** ○
- **Lincoln's Inn** ○

# I-SPY Aldwych

Start at Holborn Underground and visit the fascinating **Sir John Soane's Museum** at Lincoln's Inn before walking down Kingsway to the crescent of the Aldwych. Here you will see **Bush House**, which is the headquarters of the BBC External Services, **India House** and **Australia House**. Going east, you will see in the middle of the road **St Clement Danes**, the church of the Royal Air Force with the famous peal '*Oranges and Lemons say the Bells of St Clement's!*'

Sir John Soane's Museum

I-SPY Tick List:

- **Sir John Soane's Museum** ○
- **India House** ○
- **Bush House** ○
- **Australia House** ○
- **St Clement Danes** ○

St Clement Danes

Beyond and on the left are the **Law Courts**. Look for No. 216, **Twinings** the tea merchants on the opposite side, and **The Wig & Pen Club**, the only Strand building to escape the Great Fire of 1666. A few paces more bring you to Temple Bar which is the beginning of the City. Even now, on State occasions, the Queen asks formal permission to enter the City just as Elizabeth I did. In the Middle Ages, the heads of traitors on spikes marked the spot; today, in the middle of the road there is only the **griffin**!

*Twinings*

*Temple Bar Griffin*

I-SPY Tick List:

- **Law Courts**
- **Twinings**
- **The Wig and Pen Club**
- **Temple Bar Griffin**

# Fleet Street

No. 1 Fleet Street is **Child's Bank**, the oldest in London: Charles II, Nell Gwyn (1650-1687), and Samuel Pepys (1633-1703) were all customers. On the other side of Fleet Street beyond Fetter Lane is a series of historic lanes or 'courts' which are fun to explore: **Crane Court** where the magazine Punch was first published; **Red Lion Court**; **Johnson's Court** where you can see **Dr Johnson's House** (Dr Johnson - 1709-1784 - was compiler of the first English dictionary); **St Dunstan's Court**; **Bolt Court**; **Hind Court**; and **Wine Office Court** where you will find **Ye Olde Cheshire Cheese pub**.

## I-SPY Tick List:

- **Child's Bank** ○
- **Crane Court** ○
- **Red Lion Court** ○
- **Johnson's Court** ○
- **Dr Johnson's House** ○
- **St Dunstan's Court** ○
- **Bolt Court** ○
- **Hind Court** ○
- **Wine Office Court** ○

- **Ye Olde Cheshire Cheese Pub** ○

*Dr Johnson's House*

*Ye Olde Cheshire Cheese Pub*

# Temple

Temple

At the end of Fleet Street, turn right into New Bridge Street. Just before Blackfriars Bridge is **Black Friar pub**, full of fascinating decorations. Walk down the Embankment, turning up Middle Temple Lane on your right. You can now explore the tranquillity of the **Temple** and find the round **Temple Church** built by the mysterious Knights Templar in 1185, and heavily featured in *The Da Vinci Code*. One of those suspected of being Jack the Ripper lived in **King's Bench Walk**, so just have a quick look before making your way back up Middle Temple Lane and back into Fleet Street.

Temple Church

## I-SPY Tick List:

- **Black Friar Pub** ○
- **Temple** ○
- **Temple Church** ○
- **King's Bench Walk** ○

# I-SPY St Martin's Lane/Maiden Lane

Start at Leicester Square Underground station. The square is a pedestrian precinct, surrounded with all types of eating places and cinemas. Always busy, it is the site of many red carpeted movie premiers – a statue of **Charlie Chaplin** stands in the centre and handprints of actors and stars are set in the pavement. Walk eastwards, crossing St Martin's Lane. A pleasant detour is to go down St Martin's Lane a little way to browse in the Aladdin's cave of **Cecil Court**. Otherwise go down Garrick Street; on the right is the **Garrick Club** which has many actors and writers as members. Walk down Bedford Street, past the offices of The Lady magazine, England's longest running weekly magazine for women, first published in 1885, and turn into Maiden Lane. This is not so ladylike – in the 1630s, it was called Midden Lane, meaning dung heap! J M W Turner (1775-1851), perhaps the greatest painter England ever produced, was born and raised over his father's hairdresser's shop at **No. 26** – the old building has now gone. Look out for **Rules,** one of the oldest restaurants in London.

## I-SPY Tick List:

- **Charlie Chaplin**
- **Cecil Court**
- **Garrick Club**
- **No. 26 Maiden Lane**
- **Rules**

*Rules*

# Covent Garden I-SPY

*Covent Garden*

Turn left at Southampton Street into **Covent Garden**. This was the city's fruit and vegetable market for 300 years but is now full of shops, stalls, and street entertainers. To the west of the market square is the 'actors church' **St Paul's**. Under its portico, George Bernard Shaw's *Eliza Doolittle* was selling flowers when she was first spotted by 'Enry 'Iggins. Today, it's more likely to be home to a variety of street performers. See if you can find the memorial to the English composer, **Thomas Arne** (1710-1778) – he wrote Rule Britannia. On the south side of the square is the **London Transport Museum**, full of wonderful things to see and operate.

*London Transport Museum*

## I-SPY Tick List:

- **Covent Garden** ○
- **St Paul's Church** ○
- **Thomas Arne Memorial** ○
- **London Transport Museum** 

# I-SPY Bow Street

*Royal Opera House*

From Covent Garden, leave the market square and turn left up Bow Street. It was here that the Bow Street runners were established – forerunner of the modern police force. At the top is the **Royal Opera House**. The list of great singers and dancers who have performed here would fill a book. You may be lucky enough to hear the singers rehearsing from the little alley which runs up the side of the Opera House.

Nearly opposite is **Bow Street Magistrates' Court**. The first magistrate to preside here, in 1748, was Henry Fielding (1707-1754) who wrote the novel *Tom Jones*. Walk up Broad Court, where there is a figure of a **Young Dancer**, take a left turn, then a right into Drury Lane into Great Queen Street where you cannot miss **Freemasons' Hall** with its 60m (200ft) tall tower.

## I-SPY Tick List:

- **Royal Opera House** ○
- **Bow Street Magistrates' Court** ○
- **Young Dancer** ○
- **Freemasons' Hall** ○

# Drury Lane

Retrace your steps down Drury Lane to see the **Theatre Royal** – the largest in London with 2,283 seats and the fourth to be built on the same site. Turn up Russell Street to look into the charming Grade II listed **Fortune Theatre**. Built between 1922-24, which since the demolition of the old Wembley Stadium, is now the oldest remaining public building with a concrete facade.
Turn left into Wellington Street opposite the entrance to Covent Garden Market, to reach Aldwych and the Strand.

## I-SPY Tick List:

- **Theatre Royal** ○
- **Fortune Theatre** ○

*Fortune Theatre*

*Theatre Royal - Drury Lane*

Charing Cross station

Start at Embankment Underground, and walk northwards away from the river into Villiers Street. Before the railway was built in 1864, the area to the left was Hungerford Market, the site of the terrible (boot) blacking factory where Charles Dickens (1812-1870) worked as a boy. Nearby, spanning the Thames is the railway bridge still called **Hungerford Bridge**, flanked by two pedestrian bridges, the **Golden Jubilee Bridges**.

Further up Villiers Street on the right is **Gordon's Wine Bar**, one of the oldest in London. Climb the stairs to the Strand.

To the left, in front of **Charing Cross Station**, is a Victorian reconstruction of how the original Charing Cross may have looked. The name originates from the Eleanor Cross erected in 1291-1294 by King Edward I as a memorial to his wife Eleanor of Castile. This was the final memorial to his beloved Queen – his **Chère Reine cross**.

## I-SPY Tick List:

- **Hungerford Bridge** ○
- **Golden Jubilee Bridges** ○
- **Gordon's Wine Bar** ○
- **Charing Cross Station** ○
- **Chère Reine Cross** ○

# Waterloo Bridge

Turn right down the Strand ('strand' means 'riverbank' and, in the Middle Ages, there was nothing between this road and the Thames). On your right you will pass the interesting **Coal Hole pub**, a favourite of the Welsh poet Dylan Thomas (1914-1953). Next, on the same side, is Savoy Court, the entrance to the recently refurbished grand **Savoy Hotel** and the Savoy Theatre. A note of interest is that Savoy Court is the only street in the United Kingdom where vehicles drive on the right side of the road. Further on is the **Simpson's-in-the-Strand**, restaurant famous for its traditional English food. Across the approach to Waterloo Bridge is **Somerset House**, now a major arts and cultural centre. In winter it has an outdoor ice-rink.

*Savoy Hotel*

## I-SPY Tick List:

- **Cole Hole Pub** ○
- **Savoy Hotel** ○
- **Simpson's-in-the-Strand** ○
- **Somerset House** ○

*Somerset House*

# I-SPY Cleopatra's Needle

Return from this point by descending the steps by the side of Waterloo Bridge and walking back along the Embankment. Look for **Shell Mex House** to your right – it has the largest clock in London. You will also see the **Victoria Embankment Gardens** and, next to the river, **Cleopatra's Needle**. It dates from 1500 BC and weighs 180 tons. After a while, you are back at Embankment Underground.

## I-SPY Tick List:

- **Shell Mex House** ○
- **Victoria Embankment Gardens** ○
- **Cleopatra's Needle** ○

*Cleopatra's Needle*

*Mansion House*

Start at Mansion House Underground station.
The **Mansion House** is the residence of the Lord Mayor of London, where the Sword of State, Chain of Office, and Great Mace are kept together with other treasures. Each Lord Mayor must present himself to the monarch after his appointment in November; this is the popular pageant known as The Lord Mayor's Show and was traditionally paid for by him. Dick Whittington (1354-1423) who was Lord Mayor four times (in 1397, 1398, 1406, and 1419) must have been very wealthy indeed!
Head toward the river down Walbrook. Bearing into Cannon Street will lead you to a block of limestone on a wall at No. 111, known as the **London Stone**, which is said to be the Roman milliarium from which all distances were measured.

## I-SPY Tick List:

- **Mansion House** 
- **London Stone** 

# City Centre Map

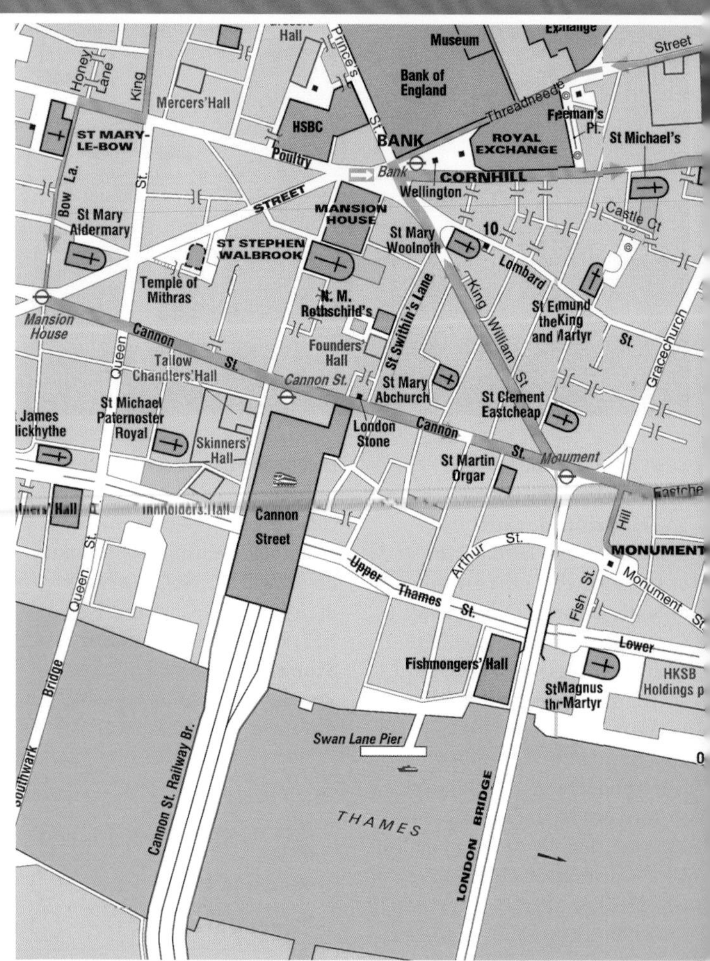

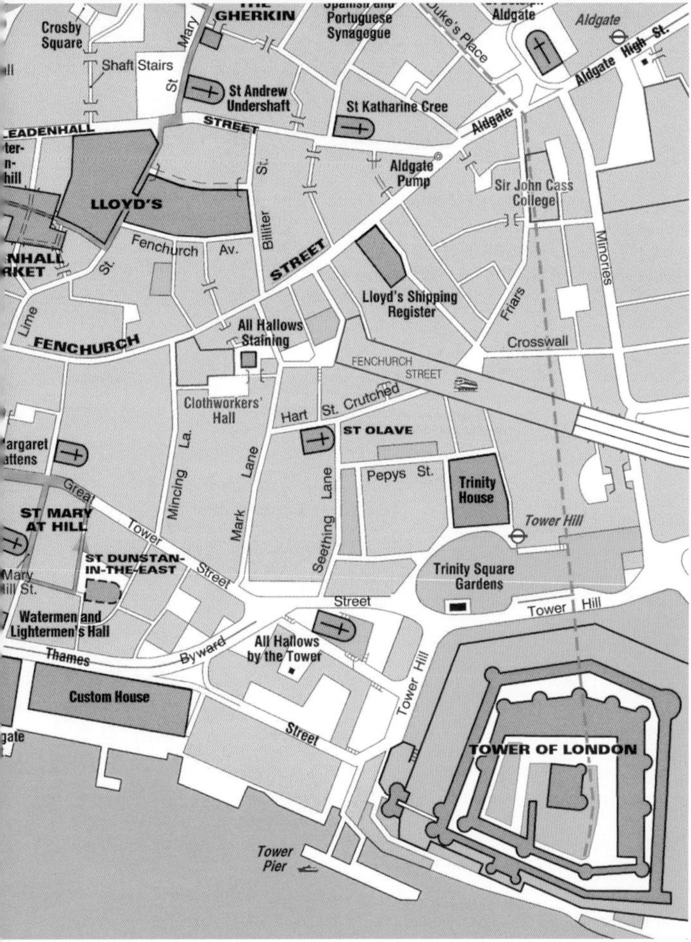

# City Centre Map

THE GHERKIN
Spanish and Portuguese Synagogue
Duke's Place
Aldgate
Aldgate
Crosby Square
Shaft Stairs
St Mary
St Andrew Undershaft
St Katharine Cree
Aldgate High St.
LEADENHALL STREET
Aldgate
Aldgate Pump
Sir John Cass College
LLOYD'S
Fenchurch Av.
Billiter St.
STREET
Lime St.
Lloyd's Shipping Register
Minories
Friars
NHALL RKET
FENCHURCH
All Hallows Staining
Crosswall
FENCHURCH STREET
Clothworkers' Hall
Hart St.
Crutched
ST OLAVE
argaret attens
Mincing La.
Mark Lane
Seething Lane
Pepys St.
Trinity House
Tower Hill
Great Tower Street
ST MARY AT HILL
ST DUNSTAN-IN-THE-EAST
Trinity Square Gardens
Mary Hill St.
Street
Tower Hill
Watermen and Lightermen's Hall
All Hallows by the Tower
Thames
Byward
Tower Hill
Custom House
Street
gate
TOWER OF LONDON
Tower Pier

# City Centre Map

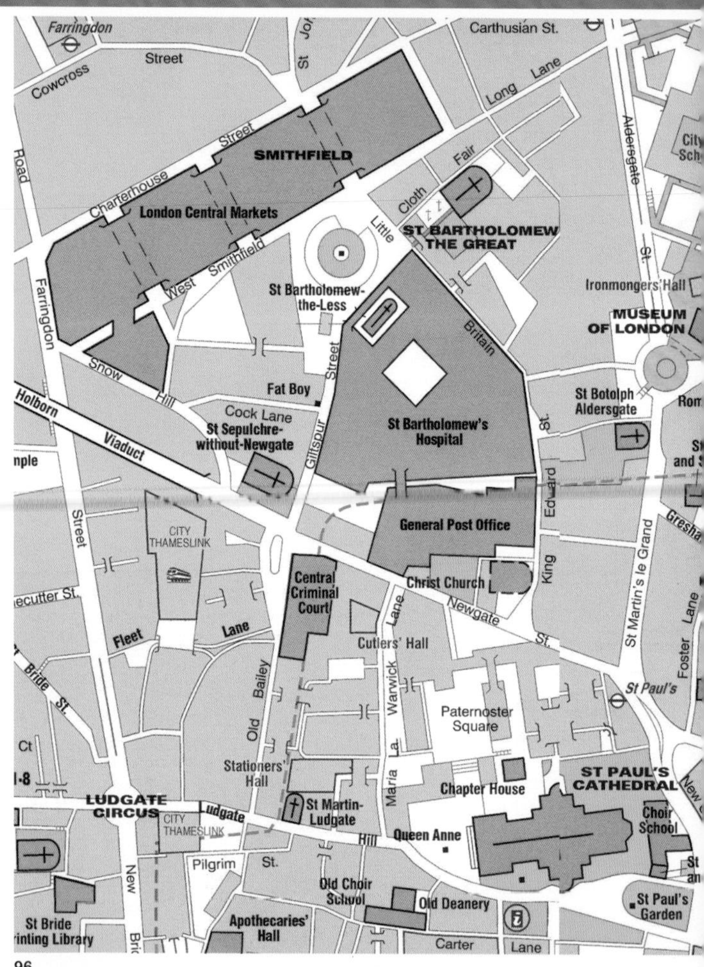

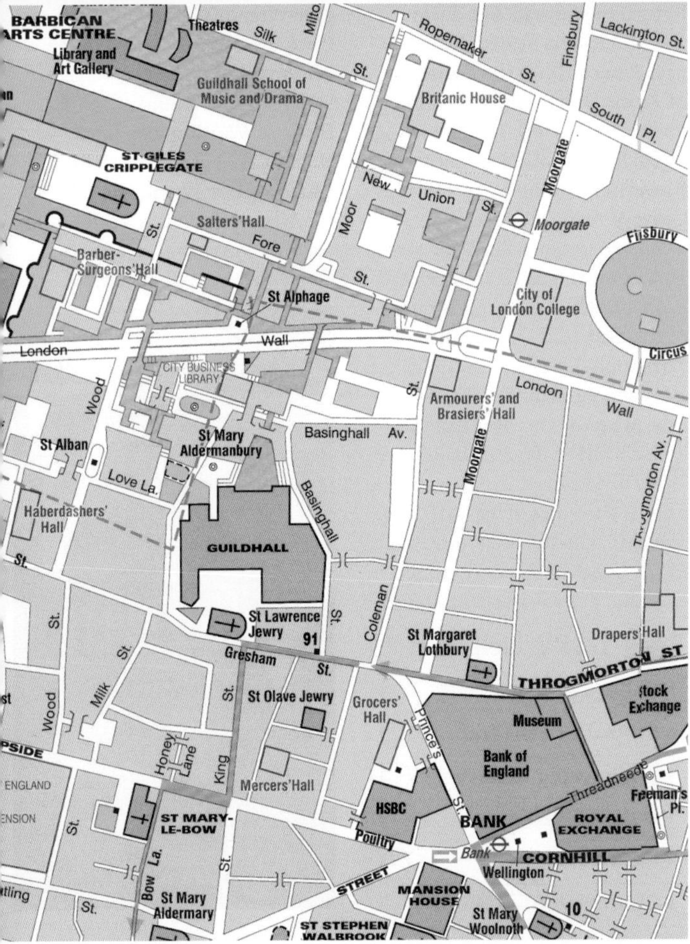

BARBICAN ARTS CENTRE
Theatres
Silk St.
Milton
Ropemaker St.
Finsbury
Lackington St.
Library and Art Gallery
Guildhall School of Music and Drama
Britanic House
South Pl.
ST GILES CRIPPLEGATE
New Union St.
Moorgate
Moor
Salters' Hall
Moorgate
Finsbury Circus
Fore St.
Barber-Surgeons' Hall
St Alphage
City of London College
London Wall
CITY BUSINESS LIBRARY
Armourers' and Brasiers' Hall
London Wall
Wood St.
St Alban
St Mary Aldermanbury
Basinghall Av.
Love La.
Throgmorton Av.
Haberdashers' Hall
Basinghall St.
GUILDHALL
St Lawrence Jewry
91
Coleman St.
St Margaret Lothbury
Drapers' Hall
Gresham St.
THROGMORTON ST
St Olave Jewry
Grocers' Hall
Prince's St.
Museum
Stock Exchange
Milk St.
Wood St.
Honey Lane
King St.
Bank of England
Mercers' Hall
Threadneedle
Freeman's Pl.
HSBC
BANK
ROYAL EXCHANGE
ST MARY-LE-BOW
Poultry
Bank
CORNHILL
Bow La.
STREET
Wellington
St Mary Aldermary
MANSION HOUSE
10
St Mary Woolnoth
ST STEPHEN WALBROOK

# St Paul's

Return to and walk left down Queen Victoria Street. Just past Peter's Hill is the **College of Arms** which, since receiving its charter from Richard III in 1484, has had absolute authority concerning family pedigrees and Coats of Arms. Return to Peter's Hill, turn left and climb the steps. This is not the usual view of **St Paul's Cathedral** but it is one of the best, and the one that Sir Christopher Wren (1632-1723) had each morning as he was ferried across the river from the house he lived in while building it. There has been a Christian church on this site since at least AD 604. The old cathedral was destroyed in the Great Fire of 1666 which gave Wren his opportunity. Once inside, climb up to the **Whispering Gallery** and also look for the monuments to the **Duke of Wellington**, **Lord Nelson** and, of course, to **Sir Christopher Wren**. His simple tomb has a Latin inscription which means '*Reader, if you seek his monument, look about you*'.

## I-SPY Tick List:

- College of Arms ○
- St Paul's Cathedral ○
- Whispering Gallery ○
- Duke of Wellington ○
- Lord Nelson ○
- Sir Christopher Wren ○

St Paul's Cathedral

From the front steps of St Paul's, walk down Ludgate Hill (looking back for the more usual view) and turn right into Old Bailey. On the right is the **Central Criminal Court** built on the site of the infamous Newgate Prison. Look on the roof to spot its crowning glory, the gold figure of the **Lady of Justice**, atop the green marble dome.

Cross over into Giltspur Street, past St Bartholomew's Hospital to **Smithfield**: London's main meat market since 1868 and the largest in the world, it has a bloody history. Mary Tudor had 270 Protestants burned here; two centuries earlier Wat Tyler, leader of the Peasants' Revolt, was cut down and killed at Smithfield in front of the curiously named **Bishops Finger pub**.

*Central Criminal Court*

I-SPY Tick List:

- **Central Criminal Court** ○
- **Lady of Justice** ○
- **Smithfield** ○
- **Bishops Finger Pub** ○

# I-SPY Barbican

Turn right and walk down Long Lane to Aldersgate and the **Barbican**, an exciting cultural, commercial, and residential complex built around the ancient **City Wall**. Walk down Aldersgate to its junction with London Wall where you will find the exciting **Museum of London**. Here you can find out more about the fascinating story of London before making your way back down Aldersgate to St Paul's.

*Barbican*

*Museum of London*

## I-SPY Tick List:

- **Barbican** ○
- **City Wall** ○
- **Museum of London** ○

The best way to explore the heart of the City of London is to start at Bank Underground Station and use the map on page 94/95 and 96/97 to help you find your own way through the maze of ancient streets and alleyways. If you can, choose a working day because only then is the City alive. Here are some of the things you should try to see but, remember, the City is a working place not a museum, and it is often not possible to enter buildings.

From Bank Underground, start your journey by walking east down **Cornhill**, once a grain market. In the centre of the road is a fine statue of the Victorian engineer **J. H. Greathead**, responsible for the deep tunnel cutting of the tube system. **St Michael's Cornhill**, on the right is built on Saxon foundations. London's first coffee house opened in **St Michael's Alley** in 1652. In 1840, the composer Felix Mendelssohn (1809-1847) played the organ in **St Peter's Cornhill**.

*J. H. Greathead*

*St Michael's Alley*

## I-SPY Tick List:

- Cornhill ○
- J. H. Greathead ○
- St Michael's Cornhill ○
- St Michael's Alley ○
- St Peter's Cornhill ○

Leadenhall Market

Lloyd's of London

Cornhill turns into Leadenhall Street and **Leadenhall Market**, dating from the 14th century and deals in high-quality meat and game. The financier, Edward Lloyd (1648-1713) started to underwrite shipping in a coffee house in 1691. His legacy, **Lloyd's of London** is now the centre of the world's insurance industry. Back at Bank Underground, **Lombard Street**, to the south-east takes its name from the Italian merchants who became money lenders here as early as the thirteenth century. Medieval bankers hung signs in the street, a practice still maintained by many banks.

I-SPY Tick List:

- **Leadenhall Market**
- **Lloyd's of London**
- **Lombard Street**

Walk down King William Street, named after William IV, King of Great Britain and Ireland from 1830 to 1837. Beyond St Clement's Eastcheap is the **Monument** to the Great Fire of 1666 which began in Pudding Lane. You can climb to the top although the view is now mostly obscured by modern buildings. Toward the river, on the west side of London Bridge, **Fishmongers' Hall** which houses one of the oldest and richest of the City's livery companies. Preserved within is the dagger with which a guild member, Sir William Walworth, then Lord Mayor, killed Wat Tyler in 1381.

*Monument*

## I-SPY Tick List:

- **Monument** ○
- **Fishmongers' Hall** ○

*Fishmongers' Hall*

Opposite Bank Underground is the **Bank of England**, affectionately known as the 'old lady of Threadneedle Street'. In its vaults are the nation's gold reserves and it alone can issue paper money. Look for the **Bank of England messengers**; they wear pink tail coats and scarlet waistcoats. At the rear is an interesting museum where you can learn about the history of bank notes and even hold a gold bar!

Further along the wonderfully named Threadneedle Street is the **Royal Exchange** which houses the London International Financial Futures Exchange. In front of it is the equestrian statue of the **Duke of Wellington**.

The **Stock Exchange** is close by, between Old Street and Throgmorton Street.

## I-SPY Tick List:

- Bank of England ○
- Bank of England messenger ○
- Royal Exchange ○
- Duke of Wellington ○
- Stock Exchange ○

*Bank of England*

*Royal Exchange*

Threadneedle Street turns into Bishopsgate where you will be able to see **Tower 42**. **St Helen's Bishopsgate** in St Helen's Place is a magnificent church known as 'the Westminster Abbey of the City'. Back on Bishopsgate is the **Temple of Mithras**, a Roman temple discovered during building work in 1954. The marble head of the Mithras found here is now in the Museum of London. From here you can see Sir Norman Foster's building at 30 St Mary Axe, the Swiss Re Building, otherwise known as **The Gherkin**.

*The Gherkin*

*Tower 42*

## I-SPY Tick List:

- **Tower 42** ○
- **St Helen's Bishopsgate** ○
- **Temple of Mithras** ○
- **The Gherkin** ○

Back at Bank Underground, walk west along the strangely named Poultry, which is where medieval poulterers plied their trade; it becomes Cheapside which was once London's greatest market - 'cheap' means to haggle. A plaque at its junction with Ironmonger Lane marks the position of the house where **Thomas Becket** (1118-1170), Archbishop of Canterbury to King Henry II, was born.

South of Poultry, on Watling Street, **St Mary Aldermary** has stained glass commemorating London's courage during the air raids of World War II, which destroyed so much of the City.

North of Cheapside, through King Street, the **Guildhall** is the seat of civic government and dates from 1411 when the City's great livery companies combined to build it. This is where all the major civic functions take place, including the sumptuous Lord Mayor's Banquet.

*Guildhall*

**I-SPY Tick List:**

- **Thomas Becket** ○
- **St Mary Aldermary** ○
- **Guildhall** ○

# Tower of London

Start at Tower Hill Underground. **Tower Hill** has seen some of the most terrible events in English history. Look for the square of paving in **Trinity Square Gardens** marking the **site of public executions**. The last executions here were held in 1780 following the Gordon Riots.
Also in this square is the **memorial to the merchant seamen** who died in both world wars.
A couple of steps down, toward the entrance of the Tower of London are two interesting Roman attractions; a replica of London's earliest **inscribed monument** and a statue believed to be of the Roman **Emperor Trajan** (AD 98-117)

*Tower Hill*

*Site of Public Executions*

## I-SPY Tick List:

- **Tower Hill** ○
- **Trinity Square Gardens** ○
- **Site of Public Executions** ○
- **Merchant Seamen memorial** ○
- **Inscribed Monument** ○
- **Emperor Trajan** ○

## Tower of London

The **Tower of London** itself is a fascinating place which played an important role in English history for more than 900 years, but it has few happy memories. Here Henry VI was murdered while saying his prayers. To this day someone comes each year from the two colleges he founded - Eton and Kings College Cambridge - to lay lilies and roses on the spot. Anne Boleyn was greeted with flowers when she came to the Tower in 1533 for her coronation; only three years later she was executed there. Brighter attractions are the **Crown Jewels** and the colourful **Beefeaters**, although the Tower's **ravens** capture the mood better.

*Tower of London*

*Beefeater*

*Ravens*

### I-SPY Tick List:

- **Tower of London** ○
- **Crown Jewels** ○
- **Beefeaters** ○
- **Ravens** ○

Tower Bridge

Leave the Tower and skirt round the outside up onto **Tower Bridge**. Its two 1,000-ton drawbridges have been raised more than half-a-million times since it was completed in 1894. The **Tower Bridge Experience** is definitely worth seeing and do not miss the view from the walkways. Recross the bridge to visit **St Katherine's Dock** down to the right.

I-SPY Tick List:

- Tower Bridge ○
- Tower Bridge Experience ○
- St Katherine's Dock ○

St Katherine's Dock

# Whitechapel

Start at Aldgate East Underground. On a Sunday morning, this part of London's East End is at its liveliest, especially **Petticoat Lane Market** which begins at the bottom of Middlesex Street and runs up to Liverpool Street Station.

Along Whitechapel High Street is the **Whitechapel Bell Foundry of Mears and Stainbank** who cast Big Ben and recast the famous bells of St Clement's. On the same side, further along you will glimpse the minaret of the **East London Mosque**.

*Whitechapel Bell Foundry*

## I-SPY Tick List:

- **Petticoat Lane Market** ○
- **Whitechapel Bell Foundry** ○
- **East London Mosque** ○

*East London Mosque*

# London Bridge

Start at London Bridge Station and make your way by the footbridge down to London Bridge City and the river where you will find **Hay's Galleria**. Behind it, in Tooley Street you will find the **London Dungeon** and Winston Churchill's **Britain at War Exhibitions**. Back on the river is **HMS Belfast**. This cruiser had a distinguished war record and opened the 'D'-Day bombardment in 1944.

## I-SPY Tick List:

- **Hay's Galleria** ○
- **London Dungeon** ○
- **Britain at War Exhibitions** ○
- **HMS Belfast** ○

*Hay's Galleria*

*London Dungeon*

*HMS Belfast*

# I-SPY City Hall

Past the battleship you come to the Norman Foster designed 'onion' hanging over the Thames. **City Hall** was opened in 2002 and is the office of the Mayor of London. In front of it you can find **The Scoop**, an open air stage where you can see live music, theatre performances and films in the summer. There are also **fountains** lit by coloured lights and open air **sculptures.**

## I-SPY Tick List:

- **City Hall** ○
- **The Scoop** ○
- **Fountains and Sculptures** ○

*City Hall*

*The Scoop*

Past City Hall is **Potter's Fields Park**, one of the few remaining green open spaces along the river. Continue under Tower Bridge to **Shad Thames** with its quaint cobbled streets, shops, and restaurants. Go back towards the bridge and cross over into **Borough Market**, the city's oldest fruit and vegetable market which was held on London Bridge itself until 1756. Almost opposite, is **The George Inn**, the only remaining example of a galleried coaching inn. The pub can count both Charles Dickens and William Shakespeare as famous visitors, but not at the same time! Nearby is **Southwark Cathedral**, a fine Gothic building that has associations with Shakespeare. Remember that this road was London's main artery for many years. Kings and armies, bishops and pilgrims and all the important figures in English history passed by here. Until 1749 **London Bridge** was the only bridge over the river and this was the main highway to continental Europe. The present bridge dates from 1973, the 1831 structure was taken down brick by brick and re-assembled in Arizona USA!

## I-SPY Tick List:

- **Potter's Fields Park** ○
- **Shad Thames** ○
- **The George Inn** ○
- **Borough Market** ○
- **Southwark Cathedral** ○
- **London Bridge** ○

*Borough Market*

*Southwark Cathedral*

## I-SPY Clink Street/Globe Theatre

Cross Borough High Street and follow Pickford's Wharf round by the river into Clink Street. The old **Clink Prison** was here, and it gave us the word meaning jail. All that now remains of Winchester Palace is the **Rose Window** of the Great Hall. Passing under Cannon Street Railway Bridge you will come to the **Anchor Inn** on Bankside with fine views of the City across the river. You are really in Shakespeare territory now. The **Globe Theatre** has been recreated just as it was in 1599.

*Clink Prison Museum*

*Winchester Palace*

*Globe Theatre*

### I-SPY Tick List:

- **Clink Prison Museum** ○
- **Winchester Palace** ○
- **Anchor Inn** ○
- **Globe Theatre** ○

# Riverside Walk

*Millennium Bridge*

*Tate Modern*

Continuing along Bankside by the river, you will come to the former Bankside Power Station, now the **Tate Modern** and the **Millennium Bridge**, offering a path across to St Paul's Cathedral. The riverside walk will eventually take you under **Blackfriars Railway Bridge**. Climb the steps up onto Blackfriars's Bridge and cross over to the Underground. On the bridge look for the splendid crest of the **London Chatham and Dover Railway**, and the well known landmark of the **Oxo Tower** on the south bank, which was built in the 1920s to advertise their product.

*Oxo Tower*

## I-SPY Tick List:

- **Tate Modern** ○
- **Millennium Bridge** ○
- **Blackfriars Bridge** ○
- **London Chatham and Dover Crest** ○
- **Oxo Tower** 

# I-SPY Southbank

Start at Westminster Underground. Cross Westminster Bridge. The **South Bank Lion** that you pass at the southern end was made for the Lion Brewery in 1837. On the Southbank you will see the imposing building that is **County Hall**. Located within it you will find **SeaWorld** and the **London Film Museum**.

## I-SPY Tick List:

- **South Bank Lion** ○
- **County Hall** ○
- **SeaWorld** ○
- **London Film Museum** ○

*County Hall*

*South Bank Lion*

*London Eye*

Right next to County Hall, dominating the whole area is the giant 135-meter (434-ft) tall **London Eye**. Opened in 2000, the 32 capsules offer truly spectacular views of London. The wheel takes 30 minutes to make one full revolution and gives great views of London especially at night.

 I-SPY Tick List:

- **London Eye** 

# I-SPY Southbank

Go under the Hungerford and Golden Jubilee Bridges. Straight ahead is the **Royal Festival Hall** and beyond that the **National Theatre**. In front of it you will find a statue of **Sir Laurence Olivier**, as Hamlet. If you explore, you will also find the **National Film Theatre**, **Queen Elizabeth Hall** and **Hayward Gallery**.

*Royal Festival Hall*

## I-SPY Tick List:

- **Royal Festival Hall** ○
- **National Theatre** ○
- **Sir Laurence Olivier** ○
- **National Film Theatre** ○
- **Queen Elizabeth Hall** ○
- **Hayward Gallery** ○

*Queen Elizabeth Hall*

*Hayward Gallery*

# The Cut I-SPY

From the South Bank, make your way into Waterloo Road which is the continuation of Waterloo Bridge. Pass under the railway bridge and you will soon see the **Old Vic**, one of London's best-loved theatres. To the left is The Cut. A little way up it is the **Young Vic**. Go to the end of The Cut to see **The Ring**, a pub with a long history and association with boxing, before returning to Waterloo Station.

*The Ring*

## I-SPY Tick List:

- **Old Vic** ○
- **Young Vic** ○
- **The Ring** ○

*Young Vic*

# I-SPY Waterloo

IMAX

Start at Waterloo Station with the enormous **IMAX** theatre outside. Leave the station and turn right down the ramp. Go left down Leake Street into **Lower Marsh Market** which is full of bustle at lunchtime. Explore the market, then go back past where you entered and turn left into Westminster Bridge Road; then fork right into Kennington Road for the **Imperial War Museum** built on the site of Bedlam, the eighteenth-century lunatic asylum, which gave its name to describe general chaos. Opposite, in Lambeth Road, is where **Captain Bligh** (1754-1817) of Mutiny on the Bounty lived. A blue plaque on the wall indicated his house.

Imperial War Museum

## I-SPY Tick List:

- **IMAX** ○
- **Lower Marsh Market** ○
- **Imperial War Museum** ○
- **Captain Bligh Plaque** ○

# Lambeth Palace

After the Imperial War Museum, cross Kennington Road and continue down Lambeth Road to the river and the Albert Embankment. At Lambeth Bridge, its entrance monuments topped with stone pineapples is **Lambeth Palace**, the London home of the Archbishops of Canterbury for over 800 years. The first was Stephen Langton (1150-1228). Next to it, and also of interest is the **Museum of Garden History**. Turn right along the Embankment to find a memorial paying respect to the **Special Operations Executive**, to those secretly recruited to perform acts of sabotage during World War II. On the opposite side of the river you will pass the Houses of Parliament before reaching Westminster Bridge.

*Lambeth Palace*

*Museum of Garden History*

## I-SPY Tick List:

- **Lambeth Palace** ○
- **Museum of Garden History** ○
- **Special Operations Executive Memorial** ○

*Thames Barrier*

This book is mainly about Central London. But look at the map on pages 124-125 to see the host of interesting places to visit on a day's outing from the centre. You can go by train, Underground, by bus, or for some destinations, use London's oldest highway – the River Thames.

River launches will take you to **Kew Gardens**. In the other direction is the **Thames Barrier** and Greenwich, where you can see the **Cutty Sark**, the **Royal Naval College** and **National Maritime Museum**, and the **Royal Observatory**.

## I-SPY Tick List:

- **Kew Gardens** ○
- **Thames Barrier** ○
- **Cutty Sark** ○
- **Royal Naval College** ○
- **National Maritime Museum** ○
- **Royal Observatory** ○

*Cutty Sark*

*Royal Observatory*

To the north of London are **Hampstead Heath**, once the haunt of highwaymen and **Highgate** with its famous cemetery where Karl Marx is buried. To the north-west is **Wembley Stadium**, the home of English football. The east of London is being radically transformed for the 2012 **Olympic** games. To the south is **Hampton Court**, the fabulous palace which Henry VIII took from Thomas Wolsey. **Windsor** is a wonderful day out. Why not use the train to get there just as Queen Victoria did?

I-SPY Tick List:

- **Hampstead Heath** ○
- **Highgate Cemetery** ○
- **Wembley Stadium** ○
- **Olympic Venue** ○
- **Hampton Court** ○
- **Windsor** ○

*Hampton Court Palace*

*Wembley Stadium*

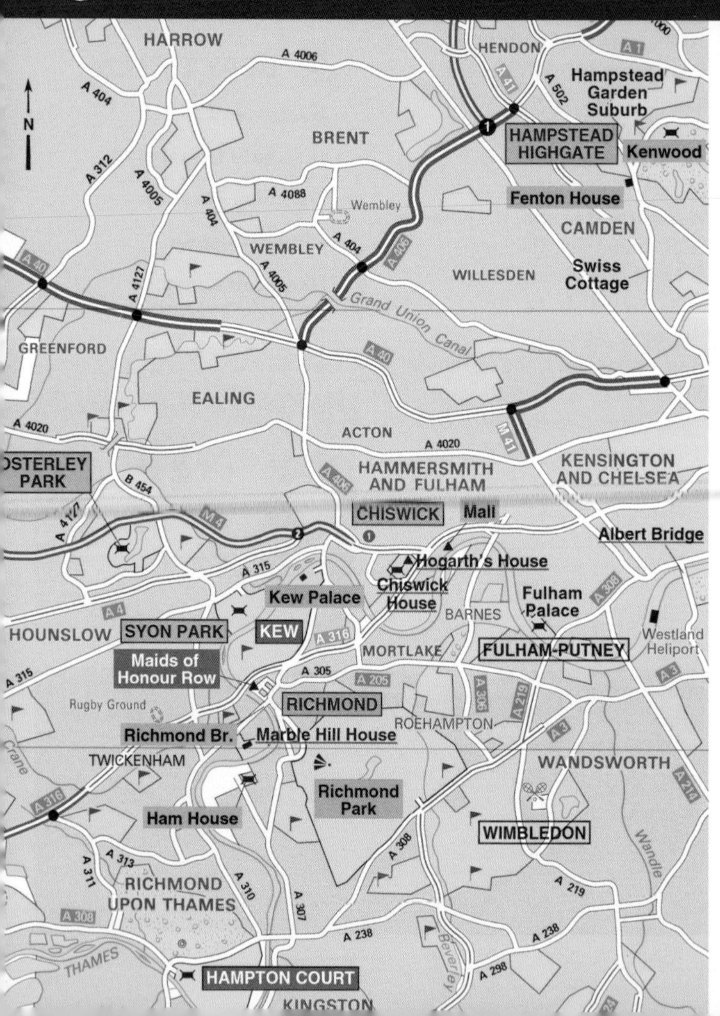
N
HARROW
HENDON
A 4006
A 404
A 41
A 502
A 1
Hampstead Garden Suburb
BRENT
HAMPSTEAD HIGHGATE
Kenwood
A 312
A 4005
A 404
A 4088
Wembley
Fenton House
CAMDEN
A 40
WEMBLEY
A 404
A 406
WILLESDEN
Swiss Cottage
A 4127
A 4005
Grand Union Canal
GREENFORD
A 40
EALING
A 4020
ACTON
A 4020
M 41
OSTERLEY PARK
A 406
HAMMERSMITH AND FULHAM
KENSINGTON AND CHELSEA
B 454
A 4127
M 4
CHISWICK
Mall
Albert Bridge
A 315
Hogarth's House
Kew Palace
Chiswick House
Fulham Palace
A 308
A 4
BARNES
HOUNSLOW
SYON PARK
KEW
A 316
MORTLAKE
FULHAM-PUTNEY
Westland Heliport
Maids of Honour Row
A 315
A 305
A 205
A 3
Rugby Ground
RICHMOND
A 306
A 219
ROEHAMPTON
Richmond Br.
Marble Hill House
A 3
Crane
TWICKENHAM
WANDSWORTH
A 214
A 316
Richmond Park
Ham House
WIMBLEDON
Wandle
A 308
A 313
A 311
RICHMOND UPON THAMES
A 310
A 307
A 219
A 308
A 238
A 238
THAMES
Beverley
A 298
HAMPTON COURT
KINGSTON

MICHELIN

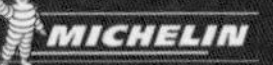

# Outer London I-SPY

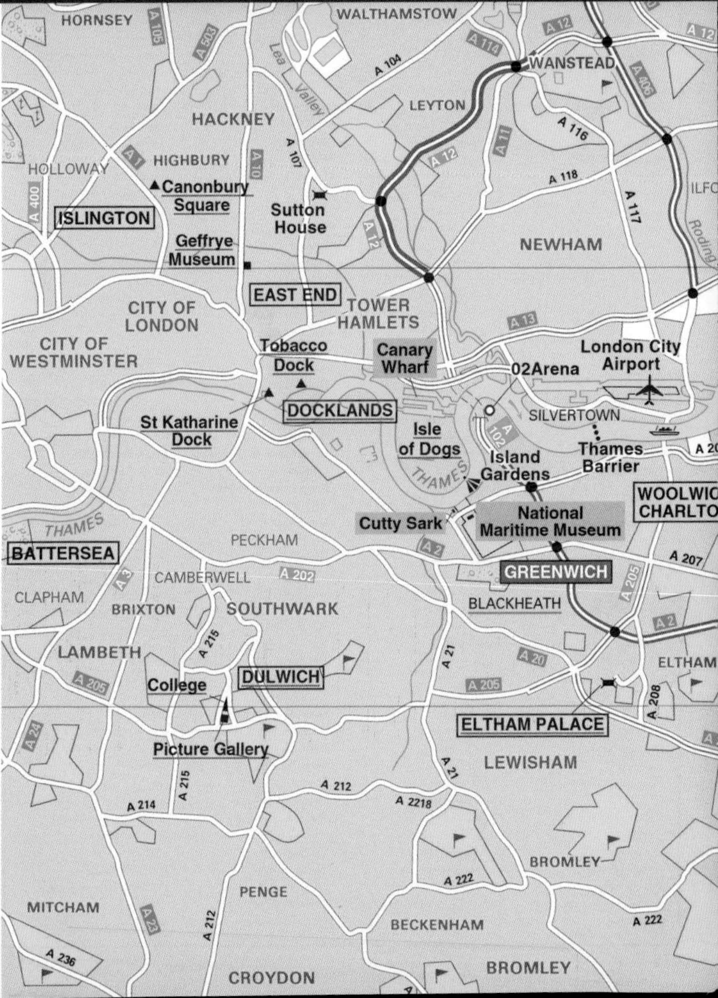
HORNSEY
WALTHAMSTOW
A 105
A 503
A 104
A 12
A 114
WANSTEAD
A 406
Lea Valley
LEYTON
HACKNEY
A 107
A 116
A 11
A 1
HIGHBURY
A 10
A 12
HOLLOWAY
Canonbury Square
A 118
ILFO
A 400
ISLINGTON
Sutton House
A 117
A 12
Roding
Geffrye Museum
NEWHAM
EAST END
CITY OF LONDON
TOWER HAMLETS
A 13
CITY OF WESTMINSTER
Tobacco Dock
Canary Wharf
London City Airport
02Arena
DOCKLANDS
SILVERTOWN
St Katharine Dock
Isle of Dogs
A 102
Island Gardens
Thames Barrier
THAMES
WOOLWIC
CHARLTO
THAMES
National Maritime Museum
Cutty Sark
PECKHAM
BATTERSEA
A 2
A 207
A 3
CAMBERWELL
A 202
GREENWICH
A 205
CLAPHAM
BRIXTON
SOUTHWARK
BLACKHEATH
A 2
A 215
A 21
A 20
ELTHAM
LAMBETH
A 205
College
DULWICH
A 205
A 208
A 24
ELTHAM PALACE
Picture Gallery
LEWISHAM
A 215
A 21
A 212
A 214
A 2218
BROMLEY
A 222
PENGE
MITCHAM
A 23
A 212
BECKENHAM
A 222
A 236
CROYDON
BROMLEY

# Index